When All Is Not Well

Om Swami is a mystic who lives in the Himalayan foothills. An advanced yogi, Swami has done thousands of hours of intense meditation in complete seclusion in Himalayan caves and woods.

Prior to renunciation, he founded and ran a multi-million-dollar software company with offices in San Francisco, New York, Toronto, London, Sydney and India.

Swami is also the author of the best-selling *If Truth be Told: A Monk's Memoir* and *The Wellness Sense*. You can connect with him on his blog, omswami.com, which is read by millions all over the world.

When

All Is Not Well

DEPRESSION AND SADNESS
A YOGIC PERSPECTIVE

OM SWAMI

Published in India by Harper Element
An imprint of HarperCollins *Publishers*

Worldwide publishing rights: Black Lotus Press

Copyright © Om Swami 2015

P-ISBN: 978-0-9940027-5-4
E-ISBN: 978-0-9940027-6-1

Om Swami asserts the moral right to be identified as the
author of this work.
Read This First is by Pixi Jane.
www.omswami.com

This work is dedicated to the welfare of all sentient beings

Asatomā sadgamaya,
Tamasomā jyōtirgamaya,
Mṛtyormāmṛta gamaya.

Take me from falsehood to truth,
From darkness to light,
From transience to permanence.

— *Brihadaranyaka Upanishad*

Contents

Read This First

For some who have never endured depression, it may seem like a creation of other's imaginations or a weakness of one's character. They may perceive it as an excuse for self-pity or an alibi for lack of motivation – a refuge for malingerers who simply can't face up to life's challenges. For anyone who has been in the grip of depression, though, it is as real as any physical disease. Depression may not be tangible like a heart ailment, but it can be just as debilitating. A touching, comprehensive description of how this malaise overtakes a person's life has been circulating on the Internet for some time, and is essential reading for those wanting to understand depression.

I've heard so many people tell those who suffer from depression to just 'cheer up'. I wonder if they can really believe that it's that simple.

Depression isn't just sadness. It is emptiness, it is misery. It is pain and nothingness at once. When you are truly depressed, you lack the ability or will to cheer yourself up. No one just 'has depression'. You suffer from it.

This is depression: you will wake at 5, 6 – maybe 7 a.m.,

feeling as though you had only just fallen asleep. It's likely you did. If you don't have to be somewhere, you could lie in bed for another three hours; too tired, too miserable and pathetic to crawl out of your bed. Or maybe you will sleep until 1 p.m., because it's so much easier to sleep through most of the day than actually live it, and you're so unbelievably tired anyway.

You will push through the day, knowing that every hour will be a struggle and not knowing how you will feel tomorrow. People will ask what is wrong, and you will simply smile and say, 'Nothing, I'm just tired.' Yes, you are tired. You are so tired of drifting through every day, with no will to actually live. But you simply smile, and they'll believe you. It's so much easier to lie anyway, and most of the time you can push away the guilt. Sometimes you might find a way out, temporary as it may be. You might write or draw or sing. Or you might cut, burn, binge, purge, drink, starve, scratch, pull, overdose ... anything to take your mind away from the utter misery it seems to be so obsessed with.

What you don't know is that soon these acts will take over your thoughts. You will spend your days not only lost in the haze of depression, but your mind will be so consumed with these thoughts of escaping and self-destruction that you think you could explode ...

You will see a series of lines, and think of the lovely scars you could make, where you will make them. Your mind will be permanently spinning with thoughts of this pain, and different ways you might destroy yourself or, more precisely, this monster inside you. But of course none of this will work. You will still spend your night alone, sitting and staring at nothing, completing mindless tasks as if they have some importance, as if you are really there. Be careful where you let your mind wander. Night time is the darkest time in depression. That's when all the demons come out, when you become weaker. It is when you will hurt yourself simply to make the urges stop for five minutes. It is when you will spend hours crying or screaming for no reason other than the agony inside. You will shake and feel as though your whole body will cave in or explode. No one will understand.

You do not have hospital beds, drips, bandages or needles to make people worry. To make them realize that this sad little girl is actually sick and needs help. Of course the depression will have destroyed any self-esteem you might have had, so you'll be too scared to ask for the help you need. You just go on, hoping someone will notice your slow, meticulous self-destruction. Don't worry: it won't always be so bad. Some days you might even feel stable. You might walk tall for one day, feeling a glint of hope that maybe one day things will get better, that things are getting better and you have the strength to fight. Then one small thing will go wrong, and you'll fall apart all over again. You feel stupid for even considering that things could get better.

Have you ever felt as though your whole body could just crumble any minute? Just crumble and fall apart, like it's lost anything it had holding it together. That's what it feels like all the time to be depressed. That raw fragility. It feels as though the smallest disruption in our life, or in your head, or in the world, could send everything spiralling downwards. And it can. The tiniest mistake can cause you to hate yourself more than you could possibly imagine. The smallest crack in your world can make it all seem pointless.

Depression destroys any resources you have. Any strength or courage you kept stored away for emergencies.

So if the tiniest little storm hits, you are left to trying to survive the ravages of a cyclone without a life boat. It wears you down and even the smallest crack can seem like an earthquake and every minute is spent waiting for the next shake. And then one day, you will find yourself curled up on your bedroom floor, sobbing, because you can't find anything to wear. Every little thing is just more proof of how worthless you are.

Eventually, you begin to expect it. You anticipate the bad times, because you know the good times are just fooling you. And they are filled with fear and anxiety over when everything will come crashing down again. You are always waiting for the next breakdown. You've become so accustomed to feeling miserable that happiness is a foreign feeling that you won't even let yourself experience. You don't deserve it. So you become numb, which at times is worse than the full-blown screaming and crying depressive 'episodes'. You find yourself begging to hurt again, because any feeling is better than feeling nothing at all.

Depression is one of the cruellest of all illnesses. You see, it's much easier to fight when you can see an end to it all. When you know that in the end you will either win or lose. But whatever the outcome, the war will be over. The thing about depression is it blurs your perception of the future and makes it nearly impossible to see that end. You start to think that there's no such thing as 'winning', and why bother fighting if you already know the outcome. It gradually strips you of any hope you previously had. And without hope, it's difficult to see a future or a reason to fight.[1]

I'm ready to move
to a place
where there is no one around.
No one to share my melodies,
and no one who speaks
my language.

I want to build a home,
a home without doors and walls.
A home without a neighbour and
a home without a keeper.

If I fall sick
I want no one around
taking care of me.
And if I die
I want no one to mourn for me.

– Ghalib[2]

1

I Am Suffering
You Need Help

The other day in the ashram, I was sitting near my window, scribbling down some thoughts on meditation. The meandering river nearby was not gently burbling as it mostly does, but roaring monstrously, the waters surging forth in its tumult. Steel-grey clouds above told of the storm beneath them, but cattle in the distance seemed oblivious to the drama, scarcely lifting their heads from grazing their lush mountain pasture.

A gale, though, swept across the landscape with all the power of nature, bending grass and swaying trees, whose branches were tossed about as if performing some violent dance. The winds had already destroyed some roses, and their colourful petals scattered ever further around the garden. While the rosebuds held out against nature's onslaught, they were nonetheless trembling, clinging to life at the end of their green stalks. Leaves were fluttering violently on a nearby tree, as if they wanted to fly away.

In the midst of all this, I saw a leaf, young and green,

succumb to the force of the wind. Ripping it from the tree, the merciless winds flung it about as if enjoying a small toy, then after some moments of indulgence, cast the leaf into a small puddle. Everything around was still the same – fluttering leaves, waving blades of grass, the rushing waters of the river, claps of thunder, swaying trees – everything but that leaf. Floating lifeless on the puddle, destiny and nature had overtaken it.

The leaf would soon start to rot, I thought. When it was united with the tree, it could gain nutrition by water, earth and sunshine. These same elements would now bring the leaf only decay. When it was a part of the tree, it was vibrantly flapping, nurtured by its connection to the greater whole, but now it was detached from life. Its source of support, strength and nourishment was gone. It had capitulated; its struggle was over.

This is depression. It is disconnection. You have lost all strength to react, fight or resist. Like the leaf, you had once tried hard to cope with life, but you could not hold on. You even tried to accept your powerlessness by playing along with the buffeting that life gave you, but just the same, you were eventually tossed to the ground. In depression, you feel utterly hopeless. Everything around you is going at the same reckless speed, but no one has cared to stop for you – and no one has picked you up. Even if you want to, you have lost the capacity to nourish yourself. You need help.

All this may not be immediately apparent, even to you. Appearances can be deceptive when depression strikes, at least in its earlier stages. Like a leaf that has just been ripped from a tree, someone in depression's thrall may look complete and alive, but is really withering inside, disconnected from emotional and spiritual nourishment. In time, however, decay will manifest, much as it does with a leaf torn from the branch. Whereas it is hard to imagine a dry, brown leaf as part of a tree bearing shade and fruit and hosting singing birds in its branches, it is almost impossible to imagine someone in the grip of severe depression enjoying a fulfilling, joyous life. It is only when someone's life withers and begins to disintegrate that we can really understand the extent of his disconnection, his depression.

Depression is not absence of happiness. It is absence of life and of will.

Someone suffering depression loses the will to do anything – even the will to live. Still, there are antidotes for depression. They are different for different people, and I've used the word 'antidote' advisedly, because depression is called *vishada* in Ayurvedic and yogic scriptures. Vishada derives from the root word *vish*, meaning poison.

Depression is toxic. Imagine the plight of those innocent victims who had to stand in gas chambers in Auschwitz and see their own and their loved ones' lives ebbing away. No matter how strong and healthy or hopeful and vital they were, breathing in the toxic gas ended their lives. Similarly, when depression takes hold of someone, her cognition and physical health is of little bearing, for depression does its own damage; it takes its own course. In the same manner that a toxicant cripples its user, depression impairs your ability to live fully – mentally, emotionally and physically. It is a toxin of the mind, and no one knows exactly how or where in the body or brain it originates.

And apart from the symptoms – which can vary greatly from one person to another – there is no conclusive way of identifying or even defining depression. I have known many people who have suffered from depression, and their symptoms ranged from a temporary loss of appetite to coming back from the verge of suicide. In some unfortunate cases, they actually took their own lives. Others were affected so badly that they quit their jobs and virtually locked themselves in their homes, in self-imposed solitary confinement.

While depression is hard to diagnose for a professional, it is equally hard for a sufferer to fathom. One of the greatest challenges for patients of depression is to pinpoint why they are depressed. Depression, it must be said, defies ordinary reasoning. For example, most patients feel terrible in the morning when they wake up and feel somewhat better as the day wears on. Thoughts of hopelessness and misery begin to consume them, though, as they lose the energy, will or even the desire to battle their depression. Just as you cannot digest dairy products if you are lactose-intolerant, you cannot stay positive when you are depressed. In fact, fleeting moments of positivity and happiness also come with the fear that the same crippling feeling will soon return, rendering you unable to even go through the motions of your daily routine.

Another baffling characteristic of depression is that it does not choose its victims against any set criteria. There is no way of saying that if you did such-and-such in your life, you will never have this disorder. In our extremely fast-paced, stressful world, anyone can be struck down by depression. Your education, faith, sexual orientation, age and marital status have no direct correlation with this disease. Among men and women, I have known atheists and believers, young and old, poor and rich – depression had them all on its database.

Nevertheless, there is one common feature among all the patients of depression I have known: the more severe their depression, the more cut off they feel from the world. Another common and most terrifying experience of depression is the feeling that it is eternal, that you may never emerge from it. It almost begins to feel like a way of life. The lurking thought that 'my depression will never end' drags most patients down more than anything else. It is a feeling that you have lost yourself, you no longer know yourself and there is no way to find yourself.

I have written this book with the intention of helping you understand how depression can take various forms, and as such, how different approaches are needed to cure different types of depression. Please note that I'm not a medical professional. I am a monk, a meditation specialist and a practitioner of yoga and tantra, who has closely worked with more patients of depression than I can count.

The lessons and learning I share in this book thus draw on information from yogic texts, as well as from my own experiences in dealing with people suffering from depression. The case studies in this book are real. To protect the privacy of the individuals concerned, their names have been changed. I have taken care to assign them names in keeping with their ethnicity to maintain the truth of their stories, because triggers of depression can vary from one culture to another.

I went out seeking love,
and with unfaltering hope
I flew so high, so high,
that I overtook the prey.

When I ascended higher
my vision was dazzled,
and the most difficult conquest
came about in darkness;

but since I was seeking love
the leap I made was blind and dark,
and I rose so high, so high,
that I took the prey.

The higher I ascended
in this seeking so lofty
the lower and more subdued
and abased I became.

I said: No one can overtake it!
And sank, ah, so low,
that I was so high, so high,
that I took the prey.

— St John of the Cross[3]

2

I Did Not Choose This

Larry, my best friend, called me one day to tell me that Anna, his live-in girlfriend, had jumped from a ferry into the waters of Sydney Harbour in a failed attempt to commit suicide. Sydney Harbour, besides being cold and deep, is known to host sharks. Fortunately for Anna, there was a quick-acting and kind fellow passenger who risked his own life to save hers. She was hospitalized, put on a prescription plan, and then discharged a few days later when things seemed okay. But as often happens with depression, things seem okay when they are anything but okay. Just as the sea is unusually calm before a tsunami, one's life can appear quite normal before depression engulfs everything.

Barely another week had passed before Anna made another abortive effort to end her life. This time, she walked right into a major traffic intersection when the pedestrian signal was still red. Miraculously, while the intersection echoed with honks and sounds of screeching tyres as cars came to a halt, there was no accident. Anna was hospitalized once again; this time, for weeks.

Larry called again and urged me to meet Anna and offer

healing, prayers, words of comfort – anything to help her live. Anna and I had shared a close rapport, so I met her after she was discharged from the hospital. During the conversation, when I asked her why she was doing this to herself, she said, 'I have to overcome my fears.'

She was twenty-seven years old at the time.

Anna was born in Poland to Polish parents. Her father had been an alcoholic and a drug addict for the greater part of his life, and her mother worked in a cafe. Hoping a change of place might help her father heal his addictions, they migrated to Germany when she was only one year old. Two years later, her mother gave birth to another child, a boy. Little changed, and Anna's father continued to struggle with his addictions. Anna's mother was unable to cope with the trials and tribulations of life, and after three years in Germany, she committed suicide. Poignantly – and adding to the emotional toll on Anna of her suicide – she left a note asking Anna to take care of her little brother. Unfortunately, Anna's father still did not become responsible. The state was eventually forced to put Anna and her brother under foster care when they were seven and four years old respectively.

While these upheavals inflicted more than ample trauma on the young Anna, life would offer no respite for her. When she was nine years old, her foster-parents migrated with Anna and her brother to Australia. The death of her biological mother, negligence of her father, her attachment with her brother, the change of family and then change of country placed an enormous burden on her. Anna's experience of life could only have been disorienting; a series of heartbreaking events that gave little chance for her to make sense of her existence. What's worse, migration brought new tribulations for her adopted family. Her foster-mother couldn't get a proper job in Australia and worked as a casual employee in supermarkets. And before Anna could settle down, less than three years later, her foster-father left his wife for another woman.

At twelve years of age, Anna was again left with her younger brother in the hands of a single parent. Their mother completely quit working. She used welfare and child support payments from the government to foot household bills, and entered into a new relationship. Her mother's boyfriend, a strapping, fifty-year-old, third-generation Australian – also living on welfare – moved in soon afterward. In Anna's own words: 'All of this had been highly inconvenient and disconcerting – but still bearable.' The unbearable was about to come. One day, her mother's boyfriend picked Anna up from school and molested her in the car. She was only thirteen years and ten months old. 'It was rough and extremely painful,' Anna would recount later.

Immediately after the incident, Anna went home and told her mother. Her mother did not move out; nor did she end her relationship with that man. All she did was have a huge argument with her boyfriend, which ended with his apology and a promise never to repeat this behaviour. Anna's mother asked her to forgive and forget and to not mention the incident to anyone. It did not stop there, though. He continued to molest her on a regular basis, totally destroying her self-esteem. For nearly four years, Anna put up with the torture before eventually moving out with her brother.

She was a mere eighteen-year-old. Although she had left her home and her foster-mother – and mustered the motivation and discipline to work various jobs to support herself and her brother – the trauma and the hurt never left her. It developed into a permanent fear in her: she was on her own, and this world had no nice people in it. A deep sense of insecurity pervaded her consciousness.

Anna got a job as a stocktaker in an electronics store where she met Larry, a computer salesman there. Larry was a soft-spoken young man who had been raised in a functional and loving family. They became good friends, partly because Larry respected her personal space. In the beginning, it was a platonic relationship. This made Anna feel very comfortable because she felt, unlike with other men, she wasn't just an object for him. He wasn't just interested in her body; he cared about her as a person. Besides healing conversations where Larry showed great empathy, eating meals, going out to movies and playing tenpin bowling together (something Anna loved) helped Anna bond with him. A few months later, she told him about her abusive past and was surprised that he didn't push her away. As is the hallmark of all great relationships, she developed deep respect for Larry. Another few months passed and after she had completely given her heart to him, she made the first move and kissed him.

Eventually, Anna and her brother moved in with Larry. Anna gradually began to see other aspects of life and come to terms with the misery of her childhood. She was not healed, though. Healing can take decades. Anna's past still haunted her, and she would regularly plunge into phases of grave depression, lasting several weeks at a stretch. The situation only worsened with time and one day, without any prior intimation, she abruptly left Larry and her brother. Larry and Anna's brother were as deeply concerned as helpless. Anna had no friends, so there was no one to call for help in locating her. After waiting for one full day, they lodged a missing person complaint with the police.

Larry and I drove around every possible location we could think of while her brother scoured the area where their foster-mother lived because other than the locality where they rented, that was the only suburb Anna was familiar with. We went to shopping malls, railway stations and parks in search of her, to no avail. She couldn't have gone far, we thought, because she had left her clothes and accessories behind. There was no clue, and the police could not trace her.

Four weeks later, I got a call from a pay phone. It was Anna, and she asked me for some money to support herself. 'I'll pay you back soon. I'm getting a job at a McDonald's,' she said. Other than saying she was in Melbourne, she would not tell me where she was; nor would she give me her address. She promised to stay in touch with me, although she didn't keep that promise. Meanwhile, we informed the police that Anna had made contact and she was okay.

A few months later, she arrived at Larry's place, barefoot, somewhat dishevelled and visibly distressed. She had just come from the Gold Coast in Queensland. She was carrying no identification. Larry called me, as he was suffering his own distress; he didn't know how to handle the situation or the best way to respond. I met Anna, gave her a hug and she began crying.

'I'm hungry,' she said.

I offered her to go out for dinner with Larry and me but she said she didn't want them to join us. She said she didn't want anything fancy and wanted to go to some nearby café for a sandwich and coffee. At my bidding, she changed into more civil attire. In the café, she told me something that Larry had failed to mention.

'I left,' she said, 'because, Larry and I had an argument,

and in a fit of rage I flung his cellphone at the wall. He was furious, and he said that I deserved all that had happened to me. My brother came out from his room and supported him, and said that he was sick and tired of my mood swings. I started crying, and Larry tried to calm me down. He said he was sorry and that he didn't mean what he said. But I didn't want to see either of them. And that's why I didn't call him from Melbourne and called you instead.'

'Even though I don't want to die,' she said, snivelling, 'the truth is, I'm actually okay with dying. I think death is the only solution to my endless problems.'

'What'll happen to your little brother, Anna? You are all he has.'

'He's not little any more,' she said. 'He can take care of himself.'

'I'm tired, Swami,'⁴ she said. 'I'm tired. Please help me if you can.'

Before I could offer any wisdom, her soft cries turned into sobs, and she burst into tears.

We were in a small café. Everyone around was looking at me askance, thinking I was the culprit of her grief. For a moment, I was undecided whether I should tell them that she wasn't crying because of me, or convince Anna to go and sit in my car, or to pacify her. I went with the latter option.

'I promise, I'll help you, Anna, but you have to listen to me.'

'What should I do?'

'Please take your medicines regularly.'

'But they only make me drowsy. I feel like a zombie all the time. I need to hold a job to pay my bills.'

'Yes, but not just medication. There are a few other

things we have to do as well. You'll be okay, Anna,' I added. 'Everything's going to be alright.'

I talked to her at length about the kind of meditation, deep breathing and activities she should do to get rid of her chronic clinical depression. She agreed to everything I said. I am not saying that deep breathing or meditation can bring anyone out of depression, but at the same time these have worked wonders for many people – Anna included. And we cannot know their effectiveness until we try them.

Having said that, it wasn't just deep breathing or meditation that cured Anna. Surely, these activities helped her in gaining physical and mental strength, in being more calm and aware of her thoughts; but what really worked wonders was something completely different. It was love; it was empathy. That's what any patient of depression needs more than anything else. It is incredibly healing when a patient feels that she is not being judged; that the person across the table understands her pain. When you reach out to someone and touch her lovingly, it releases neurotransmitters like serotonin and endorphins. Think of these as happy chemicals, imperative for combating the most harmful emotions of depression.

At the root of all emotions patients of depression experience, there are three primary feelings: first, a sense of insecurity; second, a sense of vulnerability; and finally, a sense of isolation. They feel alienated from others, as if they don't belong to anyone. Just like an open wound is susceptible to infections, a depressed mind is wounded – it is fragile and vulnerable. When you are vulnerable and when you feel disconnected, a sense of insecurity develops. You don't know how long you can go on like this; you don't know how long others will stick around for you. Your mind becomes tired and you don't want to know, leading to a sense of isolation.

Being loving and patient with someone who is afflicted with depression is absolutely critical. When someone is physically unwell, we give them a special diet, we take special care and so on. Similarly, when someone is depressed, 'special care' entails being patient, loving and non-judgemental. It's not easy, I know; sometimes, it can become overwhelming for a carer. But we ought to do at least this much for someone who is looking up to us – even if it is borne just of a basic sense of humanity.

At any rate, love, patience and empathy were the basis of Anna's healing. There were many times when Anna would procrastinate, but all it would take for her to get back to action was a loving call from Larry, me or her brother. Sometimes, we would let her feel lazy and at other times, we would urge her onward. We got her a membership at the local sports club, and she took up swimming. Not surprisingly, the high she experienced from swimming was better than that from her medicines. She began going for a swim every day. This increased her appetite and boosted her sense of self-worth too. Consequently, she was eating a healthier diet, and her body started getting the right nutrition.

Six months later, she got a job in housekeeping in a five-star hotel. With help, support, care and caution, it took Anna over three years before she could start to live her life normally. Larry played a major role in her recovery because he was there for her – physically and emotionally. She began contemplating marriage and having a family. I might add that Anna was an extremely beautiful person – inside and out. She did get married eventually and became a mother of two sons. Twelve years have passed, and Anna hasn't popped another pill for depression.

Anna's case illustrates that bouts of depression do not condemn anyone to a grim, uncertain future. Her spate of dangerous and self-destructive behaviour: jumping in the harbour, walking into fast-moving traffic or running away, were simply depression's fiendish handiwork. Of course, the seeds of her illness had long been there, with all that she had endured during her childhood; depression evinced the unresolved pain she had buried over decades.

Contrastingly, however, many patients of depression have enjoyed relatively functional childhoods, underpinning the perplexing and fickle nature of this disease. While these patients may have lived normal lives, their need for healing is no less, though, than that of patients bearing obvious scars of childhood trauma.

This is not to suggest that depression is without cause. Every episode of depression has a seed, a genesis, which is usually a painful negative emotion from the past. It could be fear, shame, guilt, anger, hatred, apathy or any other negative emotion. The seed of depression could be an experience too: even something you have all but forgotten. If you were bullied at school, for instance, you may have put up a brave face, but chances are it affected you. If you could not properly process your feelings about the bullying – if you had no one to talk to – it could easily be the cause of depression in your adult life.

It is not so much an experience itself, but how you perceive what has happened to you and the emotions you felt, that later emerge as depression. Yet there is no doubt that had you not gone through the experience, you probably wouldn't have felt that emotion. In other words, experiences can trigger emotions, and emotions – especially unmanaged or misdirected emotions – can cause depression.

One of the most terrifying things about depression is that if you have suppressed emotions and unhealed grief lurking somewhere in your mind – when you have suffered some grossly untoward incident in life and you have not allowed your pain to heal – sooner or later, it will return with a vengeance, likely manifesting in severe depression. Even beneath some of the gravest physical illnesses lies a depressed consciousness. It is simple: denial leads to disease. And while depression may visit you in severe, major or mild forms, it often catches you by stealth. In many cases, someone only realizes he is depressed when the symptoms are already wreaking havoc on his physical and emotional equilibrium.

Ayurvedic texts use many terms to define depression's symptoms. Some of them are regret (*kheda*), lassitude (*glani*), wretchedness (*dainya*), lowness (*nimnata*), languishment (*mlani*), dilatoriness and unsteadiness (*shaithilya*). I have observed that patients of depression experience most of these symptoms to varying degrees depending on the nature of their depression.

The severity of your depression dictates which of the numerous measures you can employ, and the intensity and frequency of these that would be required to overcome the illness. After all, it takes more sugar to sweeten one gallon of milk than it does for a glass. Moreover, determining the most fitting treatment requires a profound understanding of depression, and for this, knowledge of the yogic concept of three bodies is invaluable.

The yogic concept of treatment is especially powerful, because it involves healing at all levels. Merely treating the symptoms manifested in the physical body or flushing your brain with neurotransmitters is not a permanent solution. Yogic scriptures state that our physical bodies are not all there is to our existence; that there are two other bodies that make us who we are. Modern medicine has largely confined itself to the physical aspects of depression whereas it is, for the most part, an emotional and spiritual malaise.

THE THREE BODIES

Superficially, it may appear that you have a physical body and its health is directly dependent on how you keep it and what you feed it. While this is not untrue, it is not the complete truth. In fact, it is not even half the truth. Although a tiny cellphone allows us to make and receive calls, examining the structure of the cellphone alone does not give us a complete picture of its operation. There is an electrical charge in it, and a SIM card. It is communicating with the cellphone tower, which in turn communicates through a satellite. Think of your physical body as the cellphone. The software in it is your subtle body. And the electrical charge is the causal body. All three are needed for any communication to occur; and it's practically of no use if we can't make or take calls. Even with each of the three present, there need to be a communication tower, a satellite and some infrastructure. Similarly, the three bodies are constantly impacted by the environment around us. Let me explain.

The Physical Body

Your anatomical body is your physical body. It includes your cognitive, conative and vital organs. Yogic texts call the physical body *sthula sharira*: sthula means gross, carnal or physical, and sharira means body. It is also called *karya* sharira. Karya means duty or action – you perform all actions and duties on the physical plane through this body alone. It is your field of karma. This body is ephemeral and forever deteriorating, and its only truth is death.

Modern medical science prescribes physical treatments for physical ailments. Ayurveda and yogic texts approach health somewhat differently. According to their ancient wisdom, any disease appearing in your physical body is generally but a symptom of an underlying problem. The problem itself has got out of hand and expressed itself in your physical body. Such disorders could range from simple allergies to terminal conditions. They could be anything from indigestion to chronic diabetes. The physical body in itself is not the originator of the disease – it is merely the messenger. Of course, this does not apply in the same manner to diseases and infections from physical injuries. These deserve in-depth consideration of their own, and are beyond the purview of this book.

The Subtle Body

The subtle body is called *sukshama* sharira: It sustains the flow of various energies in your body, your consciousness and your intellect. Additionally, it governs the physiology of the physical body. In its absence, the physical body is a dead body, and the only reality for a dead body is disintegration and decomposition. The subtle body is invisible but has a direct impact on your physical and mental well-being. If you take care of the subtle body, your physical health improves automatically, even dramatically. When the subtle body is healthy, any food you ingest is properly processed by the body and appropriately nourishes you.

The Causal Body

The causal body is called *karana* sharira in Sanskrit. It is the foundation on which the other two bodies rest. Vedic texts state that the atman, soul, is above the three bodies, and the causal body refers to our original state of bliss. To keep things simple, however, think of the causal body as your soul. When a person dies, he is unable to respond to any stimulation. This is because the causal body (the soul) is gone and therefore the subtle body cannot function; hence the physical body is already dead. When you nourish and nurture your physical and subtle bodies, you feel more connected with your soul.

Believe it or not, your three bodies dictate almost everything that goes on in your life. They are the agents, catalysts, culprits and victims of all your experiences. They form your world of health, experiences and healing. Depression, like most other ailments, travels from the subtle to the physical body. Sometimes, the reverse may occur; what happens to your physical body can trigger depression too. For example, someone losing a limb or being diagnosed with cancer may consequently become depressed; but it is the mental and emotional response to the physical affliction that ultimately determines the severity of such depression.

Depression is a misalignment of the physical, emotional and mental energies. It is first triggered in the mind (not necessarily the brain). The mind pervades the entire body and beyond, whereas the brain is simply a processor and a warehouse of certain aspects of mind. The mind can function without the brain, but the brain is functionless without the mind. There are innumerable forms of microorganisms that have no brain tissues but have survival and instinctual skills – evidence of the existence of mind. Depression is always triggered in the mind first – in the subtle body – and when it is not treated, it migrates to the physical body.

Before we can begin exploring various ways of treating the illness, it is extremely important to know about the different kinds of depression. A treatment that is appropriate for one kind of depression may be counterproductive for another; worse still, it may even cause harm to the patient. Depression exists in a myriad of forms and degrees, and selecting an appropriate treatment – as with all illnesses – hinges on a proper diagnosis.

The dismal situation waste and wild,
A dungeon horrible, on all sides round
As one great furnace flamed, yet from those flames
No light, but rather darkness visible
Served only to discover sights of woe,
Regions of sorrow, doleful shades, where peace
And rest can never dwell, hope never comes ...

– John Milton[5]

3

Please Kill Me
Severe Depression

Tim was born in a Catholic family in a small countryside town in New Zealand. He was brought up by a single mother because his father had abandoned them when he was just three years old. His father left home on the pretext of buying groceries but called from a public phone saying he wasn't coming home. His departure from their lives was totally unexpected. They couldn't locate him, and he never made contact again. His mother couldn't forgive her husband, and she never remarried. This traumatic incident embittered her, and she held Tim responsible for his father's deserting them.

'I couldn't take care of your father ever since you were born, and that's why he left us,' she would say to Tim at every opportunity, even when he tried to comfort her. 'I'm living only because you're my responsibility. I would be long dead otherwise,' she said whenever she was stressed – which was almost every day. On days when she was in a good mood, she would otherwise declare, 'I'm living only because of you. You are all I have.'

As a child, Tim had to bear the enormous burden of acting like an adult – to pacify his mother, to be there for her, to listen to her – to fulfil the role his father had abjured. It was, suffice it to say, a weird relationship. On the one hand Tim's mother was deeply attached to him and wouldn't even permit him to do sleepovers at his friends' homes. Indeed, she wouldn't allow him to be away from her any longer than a couple of hours; and certainly never past sunset. She would say that she loved him so much that she couldn't bear to be separated from him. On the other hand, she constantly told Tim how he had ruined her life and how she didn't want to live. He suffered the tyranny of his mother's emotional incontinence; the nature of the words she uttered was entirely dependent on her mood and her psychological state at the time.

Tim nevertheless wanted to be everything for his mother and do everything for her, because he thought this would make her happy. This way, he reasoned, his mother wouldn't see him as a burden. Against all odds, he maintained good study habits and excelled at school. After high school, he wanted to enrol in a university. This would mean leaving his small town and moving to one of the bigger cities. His mother was aghast at the prospect of his leaving her. But he quietly applied at a university of his choice, thinking his mother would surely let him study if he got a place in his desired course. He wanted to be an architect.

Three weeks later, the postman delivered a letter for Tim when he wasn't home. Seeing the logo of some university on the envelope, his mother immediately opened it. All hell broke loose as soon as she read the letter. The university had offered him a place. She called each of Tim's friends in a desperate attempt to find him. Two hours later, he arrived home to find his hysterical, drunken mother sitting at the kitchen table. She accused Tim of being just like his father, and she cried uncontrollably and bashed her head against the kitchen door. Tim stood in a corner throughout his mother's extravagant remonstrations, shocked and scared. 'If you step out of this town, I'll kill myself,' she said. 'You can work in the farms or get a job at the supermarket, but you are not leaving this town. Don't you dare be like your father.'

Over the next few days, Tim tried his best to prevail upon his mother. Every time he broached the topic of his study, though, she would react violently. After some time, Tim concluded that he would never sway his mother on this, and ditched his plans for higher education and architecture. He began to hate everything his mother liked – including church. Even the pancakes and crumpets he had relished since he was a child lost their appeal, because his mother wanted to make them for him and eat them together. Like his mother, Tim had given up on his life and dreams. And then something quite unforeseen happened.

The International Society for Krishna Consciousness, or ISKCON as it is commonly known, is the organization behind the Hare Krishna movement in the West. Tim heard about a newly built ISKCON temple in another small town closer to Auckland, which was approximately sixty kilometres from his home. One of his friends took him there and Tim, now nineteen years of age, was absolutely mesmerized. There was only love in the air; love for God. There was no stress – no one was shouting or yelling. Devotees were smiling and laughing: clad in vibrant saffron, they danced in ecstasy. This was markedly different from the staid church environment Tim had experienced since his early childhood.

'Krishna is God and he'll rid you of your suffering,' a monk told him there. The monk's forehead was adorned with a long tilak and his head was shaved. He was wearing tulsi beads around his neck and a small pouch in a sling hung from his neck, touching his chest. One of the monk's hands was in the pouch; he was constantly chanting the Hare Krishna mantra with the chanting beads in it.

For the first time in his life, Tim experienced peace. For the first time in his life, he had vegetarian food, and it tasted so different to what he had been eating for the preceding nineteen years. Tim was captivated by the movement, and he underwent initiation just a few months later – much to the chagrin of his mother. She resented his becoming a vegetarian and forgoing the Catholic way of life.

She told Tim that if he didn't return to the Catholic Church, she would stop eating food altogether. Tim didn't return to the church. She continued eating. She then told him that she would take her own life if he didn't stop visiting the Hare Krishna temple. Tim didn't stop visiting the temple. She continued living. Deeply influenced by the philosophy of karma and teachings of ISKCON, Tim began to come to terms with his life.

But this feeling of peace was somewhat illusory. He had only found temporary comfort, for he was not really healed. ISKCON had only helped him put his pain on the back burner. Only love and acceptance could have healed him, because his difficulties in life stemmed from a lack of these in the first place. At ISKCON he felt accepted, and that acceptance had boosted his spirits. Yet his life was not complete. Love of God is divine, but there are some things only a human touch can accomplish. You can hug, kiss, caress or adorn a book or an idol, but it doesn't hug you back. It shows no empathy, no emotions.

As another couple of years passed and Tim grew spiritually, he began seeing his mother's tantrums as control tactics; and becoming weary of them, he decided to move to Australia, to ISKCON Sydney. His mother flew into a rage at the news, and tore off Tim's saffron robes. 'I promise, I'll kill myself instantly if you leave this town,' she threatened.

Tim truly wanted to be there for his mother, but the eternally tense and demanding environment at home had become intolerable for him. Fully convinced that his mother would actually end her life if he left, he tried to stay with her, but couldn't. Eventually, he told her that he was leaving for Sydney – and nothing could make him change his mind. He understood that he may have to live with the guilt that he could have saved his mother's life by not leaving her. Yet Tim chose to take this risk rather than endure his toxic domestic situation any longer.

Tim moved out and moved on. And what of his mother? She never made any attempt to take her life. Even two decades later, she was still behaving in just the same manner: she remained dry, difficult and insufferable. In Tim's words, 'There was perhaps never a phone call where she didn't accuse me of being the cause of her misery. I was too small to remember anything when my father left us, but somehow I think I know why he left. She's just too demanding and unbearable. It's impossible to talk to her. I hope one day Krishna blesses her.'

Tim started selling ISKCON books in Sydney to spread the word of Krishna's love and to pay his bills. There wasn't much money in this, though, so he took a job at the local supermarket again. Four years ticked by. Everything seemed fine, and Tim was starting to find his feet. He opened up his heart to a girl, another full-time devotee, and they decided to marry. While ISKCON had helped Tim, and while he was away from his mother and seemed peaceful, internally he was anything but at peace.

Tim was fearful to the point of distraction about entering into a committed relationship with a woman, and remained deeply conflicted. ISKCON permits sex only between lawful partners, and two devotees can court for a period of six months, within which they must decide if they want to consummate the relationship. Tim's fears got the better of him, and he backed out at the last minute. In his words, 'I didn't think I could keep her happy. Anytime she tried to protect me, even out of love, I got scared because she reminded me of my mother. I thought it was best to stay away.'

This incident, however, sent him spiralling towards the dungeon of depression. Tim felt that he had betrayed this girl, and losing his self-esteem and confidence, he quit his job and began to draw unemployment benefits. He ceased attending the temple, stopped telephoning his mother and completely avoided socializing. The only time he would emerge from his self-imposed exile from the world was to either buy groceries or to visit his psychiatrist. The latter was absolutely necessary, because Tim had become dependent on Valium to keep himself on some semblance of an even keel, and Valium is a prescription drug. Perhaps unsurprisingly, his physical condition deteriorated badly under this regime. Tim was six feet tall and weighed 160 pounds when he arrived in Sydney. Within four months of the onset of his illness, he had gained an unhealthy fifty pounds.

A number of ISKCON devotees got together to help him in whatever way they could, but Tim mostly remained depressed. One fine morning, he awoke with a severe backache. There really was no rational explanation for the pain, but after initial treatment lasting a few months, he was placed on disability benefits by the state.

This stultifying existence continued for more than a decade. All this while, Tim remained mostly confined in his apartment, and he developed diabetes and high blood pressure and suffered from chronic insomnia. He was administered prescription drugs for each of these conditions. Moreover, year on year, his dose of Valium was increased because he became desensitized to the drug, and his existing dose failed to bring him relief. On numerous occasions, he would take more than the prescribed dose just so he could fall asleep. Strangely, his psychiatrist would simply write him a new prescription whenever he ran out of the drug – an action that was as cruel as it was unethical – despite being well aware that Tim had overdosed.

Eventually, Valium became almost ineffective. But Tim figured out another, self-destructive idea: he mixed wine with Valium. This allowed him to forget about everything – his life and himself – completely. Resort to the dangerous cocktail of alcohol and tranquilizer led to periods of blackout. Tim routinely overdosed with the intent to sleep forever. His routine prayer was, 'Please kill me, Krishna. Let the overdose work this time. Let me not wake up. I'm tired.' Call it destiny or miracle, he never succeeded at taking his own life. Countless times, ambulances came, and so many times he was found unconscious in his apartment; but each time he survived.

His numerous escapes from death by overdose, though, were not so much due to luck but divine intervention in human form. A female Krishna devotee, Vrinda Devi Dasi, was committed to helping Tim. She saw him daily, made meals for him and even at times, did grocery shopping for him. He began feeling comfortable in her company. Vrinda's friendship persisted, even after many devotees had already shunned Tim upon discovering that he was imbibing alcohol. Consuming alcohol is against one of the four fundamental precepts of ISKCON: no illicit sex, no meat eating, no gambling – and no intoxication. Disregarding the other devotees' judgements, Vrinda did not give up on Tim. She would make him go out at times and have a coffee (generally also prohibited in ISKCON). With her care and acceptance, the spark of life was beginning to flutter once again in Tim; the lotus in his chest was blooming again.

That being said, Tim was still far from well by any definition of the word. He was not ready to exercise yet, his backache persisted and he was in no shape to work. But his desire to live was rekindled. This is the first important breakthrough for a person who is emerging from depression: a happy yearning for life sprouts in his heart, and he truly wants to be happy again.

Furthermore, Tim could envisage a future with Vrinda by his side. She wasn't pushy: she gave him his personal space, she didn't judge him; and above all, she was patient with him. This was how Tim saw love, because this is exactly what his mother didn't give him – personal freedom, the right to live. Love heals like nothing else. And the definition of love varies from person to person. Whatever we feel we lack in life, whenever anyone gives us that, we equate it with love. It could be attention or intimacy for some or appreciation and spending quality time for others. Love is different things to different people.

Tim stopped drinking wine and gradually, over five long years, weaned himself completely off Valium. He lost twenty pounds in seven months just by being positive, eating well and on time – and being happy. As he lost weight, his back pain eased and he started doing light exercise. He resumed his regular prayers at the temple, and he would never miss his long morning walk. None of this would have been remotely possible without Vrinda's love and care.

You and I can only hope to understand what Tim went through in the decade in which he languished with depression. And there's nothing to say that he won't be struck with depression again; and no guarantees that any subsequent episode wouldn't be as debilitating as the first. The circumstances of each patient are unique, and it would be naïve – if not downright ignorant – to think that we can either define and categorize depression in absolute terms or come up with an all-encompassing system to cure it. There are numerous physical, psychological and physiological factors that contribute to a patient's condition of depression.

One common, vital factor nonetheless aided the many people I know who have climbed out of depression's abyss: the support of their families and loved ones. This support was not limited to just being there for them. It was thoughtful, caring support. For instance, the family and friends of someone suffering from depression should not say 'you are not depressed' or 'you don't have depression'. Nothing hurts a patient of depression more than hearing, 'there is nothing wrong with you'. When you are depressed, you know that something is wrong with you; you are not making it up – you are not simply being pessimistic or negative. The doom and gloom in the world appears so real that when anyone tells you that you are not depressed, you immediately distance yourself from that person. You cannot help but feel that they, like most others, don't really understand you or what you are going through.

The reason I have cited Tim's case in this chapter is because I want you to know three things about depression, especially severe depression. First, if you neglect or suppress yourself for too long – if you deprive yourself of love and care and if those around you constantly demean you, destroying your self-esteem – in all likelihood, you will become mired in severe depression; and it will take quite some time to free yourself from it.

Second, when anyone around you starts to show the physical symptoms of depression, they need your care and attention. Along with medication, love and care are the two most important healing factors.

Third, depression is a very real condition; it is not about someone being negative or melodramatic. Just like any other serious illness like cancer, depression is an illness.

When the illness is severe, cognitive and behaviour therapies won't be sufficient to combat it. Nothing on its own will suffice, for that matter. You are most unlikely to transcend a serious bout of depression by just meditating or practising yoga. When the condition becomes physical, you would likely need medication. Although I'm not a fan of antidepressants, a patient suffering severe depression should usually take them.

These drugs must never be viewed as a panacea, however. A plan to come off them is essential, because in the longer run, they do more harm than good. I'll talk more about this later in the book. For now, let me share with you the symptoms of a severe episode of depression. Other than a desire to cease living, a patient can easily experience some or all of the devitalizing symptoms that depression engenders.

The first thing depression affects is your sleep. Patients of depression often suffer from hypersomnia or insomnia (too much or too little sleep). What's particularly disturbing is that often they will alternate between the two: on some days they'll feel like not sleeping and on other days, they may feel like not getting out of bed at all. The most common symptom is the inability to sleep till it's very late at night and then feeling too exhausted to rise in the morning. If you are particularly blighted by depression, you often just don't want to wake up. It is not uncommon then to feel the need to stay in bed until late in the afternoon.

Other symptoms of depression may include, but are not limited to, excessive fatigue, wild mood swings and a constant anxiety lurking at the back of your mind. When you are depressed, one moment you'll feel that you are fine and that you have come out of your depression. You will get up and walk around with hope and confidence, only to experience a sudden relapse just a short while later. A good deal of the anxiety in depression comes from the uncertainty it evokes: you just don't know if you are actually okay, or merely feeling okay for the time being.

Unsurprisingly, given that you may suffer from distorted sleep patterns, fatigue and anxiety, depression is highly detrimental to your mental focus and attention span. It can cause what is sometimes termed 'cognitive fog' in allopathic medicine. Cognitive fog, also known as clouding of consciousness or mental fog, is a condition where normal functions of your consciousness such as thinking, remembering and reasoning are affected, and in severe cases, you experience a sort of derangement. Additionally, depression can cause, or at the very least contribute to, the following conditions:

- A decline in the production of sexual hormones in males and females, leading to either a reduction in sexual appetite or a complete loss thereof;
- Hypotension or hypertension (low or high blood pressure);
- Hypothyroidism or hyperthyroidism (low or high levels of thyroid hormones);
- Obesity (unhealthy weight gain);
- Weight loss;
- Bulimia or anorexia (binge eating and purging or starvation);
- New allergies, inflammatory diseases and asthma; and
- Insulin resistance, causing high blood sugar levels.

Any form of depression experienced by the body is almost certain to impact your digestive system, because Ayurvedic and yogic texts state that the stomach is the seat of fear and stress. Therefore, patients of depression often experience irregular bowel movements, along with the range of symptoms they experience in other parts of their being. Even with all or some of the symptoms above, you shouldn't immediately label your depression as severe (what's left you may wonder, I know). Read on.

The mark of a moderate man
is freedom from his own ideas.

Tolerant like the sky,
all-pervading like sunlight,
firm like a mountain,
supple like a tree in the wind.

He has no destination in view
and makes use of anything
life happens to bring his way.

– Lao-tzu[6]

4

What the Hell Happened?
Major Depression

The ancient Chinese philosopher Lao-tzu left us pearls of wisdom that transcend culture, time and context. Indeed, if you adhere to his words, it is hard to imagine anything but contentment and freedom from inner turmoil. His understanding of human nature and the eminent practicality of his writings give us insights for avoiding the inner conflict that can lead to depression. A quote attributed to Lao-tzu that is most pertinent for those suffering from depression says, 'Life is a series of natural and spontaneous changes. Don't resist them – that only creates sorrow. Let reality be reality. Let things flow naturally forward in whatever way they like.'

If only it were that simple.

Most of us have our own ideas, thoughts and desires around how our lives ought to be, but our lives rarely unfold that way. When life springs a surprise on you – an unpleasant surprise – your first reaction is disbelief: 'How could this happen to me?', followed by denial: 'This can't happen to me.' All ailments originate between denial and disbelief. If you can just be open and willing to see what purpose life might have the way it's unfolding for you, rather than resist and oppose it vehemently, you may find there's no struggle. Floating with the current is effortless; it's when you swim against it that you have to gather all your might.

This is where depression can find unlikely victims. While the 'please-kill-me' type of severe depression often hits people because they have had difficult childhoods or endured trying circumstances over a long period of time, major depressive episodes can seem to ambush those who have enjoyed relatively uncomplicated lives. Depression usually strikes such people because they are caught off-guard by life; they are unable to proceed beyond denial and disbelief, or the pain in the aftermath of some traumatic happening.

Getting beyond denial and disbelief is only part of the healing process arising from a painful experience. Once you go past disbelief, you get to the next difficult question: 'Why did this happen to me?' The more you ask this question, the more questions arise. Though confused and tired, you muster your courage and inner strength to come to terms with the unexpected – you somehow manage to absorb the surprise. But you are not healed yet and because the surprise was so sudden, unexpected and nasty, it leaves a permanent imprint on your mind in the form of a fear: 'What if it happens again?' This is where depression emerges – major depression. You ask yourself, 'Where am I going wrong? Why can't I feel like I used to? Will I ever be the same again?' The longer you ponder these questions, the harder it is to come out of depression.

You feel trapped and helpless, like the leviathan elephant that is cowed into submission by a small goad. You still have strength and abilities, but the tiny piercing of the goad is so powerful (the unpleasant surprise) that you just bow down and submit. Deep somewhere the giant in you knows that you are much stronger than the mahout, and you are far bigger than the goad; but recalling the pain and the fear of that pain being inflicted again enfeebles you.

At such times, shifting your attention or investing your energies elsewhere remains the only sensible solution. Like Oscar Wilde said, 'All of us are in the gutter but some of us are looking at the stars.' Pain may linger for a little while, but suffering starts to subside when you accept: 'Fine, it has happened now. Let me deal with it. I'm not going to let my past ruin my present or dictate my future. I've come to the realization that it's not the goad (event) itself but the mahout (life) who is causing my pain. And I have only two options: either I break free and go to live in the woods where I belong or I negotiate with the mahout.' This breaking free has nothing to do with the physical world; it is but a mental perspective. When you negotiate and accept terms, healing begins.

When someone encounters a tragic event in her life – ranging from failing an exam to losing a loved one, or being unsuccessful in love, being harmed, cheated or losing money in stocks – she can easily fall into a depressive state. Such events can lead to anxiety attacks or a temporary manifestation of the symptoms as outlined in the previous chapter. Whereas severe major depression can take years to overcome, symptoms of depression triggered by a traumatic event generally disappear within a few months. Coming out of such depression depends largely on a patient's mental set-up and support from his family and friends. And the greatest support you can extend to a patient of depression is acceptance. Accept and understand that she is not intentionally behaving in a dysfunctional manner. Something deep within is broken which is making her behave like this.

There are two vital things you should know about depression of this type. First, it is often episodic. Those who don't completely overcome it the first time tend to suffer another episode within a few years. When you continue to live a stressful or an unstable life, subtle undercurrents of emotional turmoil are always threatening your mental equilibrium. Often the melancholy experienced during the first episode of depression leaves a lasting imprint, in the form of chronic ailments in the physical body or a lingering fear and insecurity in the mind, making the person ever more vulnerable to relapses.

In this sense, it is rather like the aftermath of a physical injury. If you fracture your arm, the doctor will put it in a cast. It will ache, and for the time it is immobilized in plaster, your freedom will be restricted. Later, when the cast is removed, you naturally remain cautious with your arm, because the healed bone is still fragile. It is not ready to take another blow. Depression is a fracture of not just your mind, it's a fracture of your very being – everything you thought you were or stood for feels broken.

Second, the tiniest incident – even what may appear to others a harmless surprise of everyday life – can trigger it. It can happen to anyone – you, me, anyone. To perfectly normal people enjoying fine health and leading perfectly normal lives. Even if you were brought up well and had caring parents and siblings; if you were not bullied in school and did not face any major failures in life – and if, all in all, you lived a veritable dream life – depression can strike as implacably as the tax man collecting arrears. It can be so swift and sudden that you are left wondering 'what the hell happened?' There are many probabilities, many theories and many potential reasons; but there's no real answer. Just as the finest, fittest, athletes can die from heart attacks or succumb to cancer, anyone can be hit by depression.

A case in point is Rashmi. Rashmi had enjoyed a blissful childhood. She was the youngest of three siblings, and her parents had absolutely doted on her. She was full of self-confidence, high on self-esteem; all in all, a very positive and accomplished person. Rashmi lived in Switzerland. She was a first-generation immigrant. Forty years old at the time, Rashmi was a happy mother of two daughters. With two professional degrees and working as a senior finance manager for a world-class investment bank, Rashmi was doing exceedingly well in her career. She had a supportive and loving husband who was the CEO of a public company.

Rashmi's family would go for regular family vacations and dine out frequently in the most salubrious establishments. Other than their own home, which they owned outright, Rashmi and her husband owned a farmhouse in the countryside. They also held a sizable portfolio of investment properties and drove expensive cars. They had no debt – not even credit card debt – and no financial or personal challenges to speak of. Rashmi's elder daughter had just secured a place in medical college, and her younger daughter was a talented kathak dancer who had already won numerous awards and given several public performances. Rashmi's family life was of the kind that advertisements go to great lengths to portray – only it was real. Heck, even the family dog, a cute Chihuahua, played his part in this idyll, performing summersaults on their lawn while they enjoyed their organic breakfast on lazy Sunday mornings. Life couldn't get any better. All was perfect; or so it seemed.

At five feet six inches, Rashmi was an attractive, well-endowed woman in top physical shape. She exercised regularly and played tennis on the weekends. On most mornings, she would have eggs for breakfast and about thrice a week she would eat chicken. The rest of the time, she ate vegetarian food. I've deliberately mentioned her dietary habits because eggs and chicken are acidic in nature, and people with acidic diets are more prone to physical disease than those on an alkaline diet. Rashmi had been eating a similar diet for nearly thirty-eight years though, and she only consumed meat and poultry in moderation. So in principle, there appeared to be no issue with her health. Until one day, that is.

Rashmi went out one evening for a colleague's farewell dinner with her team from work. She ate a fairly normal Western dinner – a Caesar salad, gnocchi in pesto, followed by a chocolate pudding with a cappuccino – and drank a glass of red wine. An hour after she returned home, she experienced heartburn. She had never suffered this before, and thought it would subside on its own. It didn't. She tried a couple of home remedies without any success. Not thinking much of it, she went to the local pharmacy and bought an off-the-shelf antacid. This gave her some relief – just enough so she could get some sleep.

The next day at work, at around 11 a.m., her heartburn returned with a vengeance. She took another antacid and skipped her lunch, but the condition only worsened in the afternoon. She consulted her family doctor, who told her that the heartburn was nothing to worry about and prescribed her strong antacids. 'It's just bad reflux,' he said. 'It'll go away in a day or two.' Another couple of days passed, and the prescription drugs made not an iota of difference. She was beginning to worry. In the mornings she would rise feeling well, and as the day progressed, her heartburn would just worsen.

She visited her doctor again. He ordered a barrage of tests and increased the potency of the antacids. All the test reports returned negative. There seemed to be no rational explanation for her condition. The doctor was nonplussed, and couldn't offer Rashmi any helpful advice. She was even more perturbed now because the reports indicated she was okay, yet she was not feeling okay. Simple heartburn was driving her to distraction. Every morning she would awake free from gastric pain, and regardless of what she ate for breakfast, heartburn would return by 11 a.m. The pain would peak by 2 p.m. and remain until late evening.

Rashmi was referred to a gastroenterologist who did further tests, recommended some dietary changes and put her on a new prescription plan. She tried eating slowly, she tried chewing more, she drank lemon water and she tried sipping cold milk. Nothing worked; her condition did not improve in the least with any of these measures. She became depressed, and took one month's leave from her work. Perhaps she was fatigued from working all these years, she reasoned.

During this whole month, she suffered every day in the same manner: free of pain in the morning followed by severe heartburn throughout the rest of the day. Depression engulfed her life completely, and she now dreaded every moment of living. Even the hours in the morning where she had some respite from the heartburn brought terror, because she knew it would be 11 a.m. soon.

She resumed her job after a month but she felt it a challenge to even get out of bed in the morning, let alone work the whole day. She resigned, but her employer persuaded her to assume a part-time role until she was well again. She agreed, only to quit four weeks later. Nearly three months had passed and in Rashmi's words, she was 'going mad'.

Everything around her and about her began to haunt her. She no longer liked herself, her body, home, husband, kids or dog. Everything looked alien and disturbing. She was angry and anxious all the time. She stopped going to the gym and shunned playing tennis. She would skip her meals as much as she could, because eating a meal would make her reflux even worse. 'My own daughters and husband look like strangers to me,' she would tell me later. 'It's such an unreal feeling. When I see them, I feel like I don't know them. I don't like it when they are smiling or laughing. I feel I'm in my home, but they are strangers here. I don't know why they want to talk to me or have dinner with me. I don't feel like talking to them at all. I'm really worried because I know they are my family, but I don't feel that connection any more.'

Her daughters and husband convinced her to go on a family vacation, in the hope that a change of scene would help her. She agreed, but the vacation proved a bad idea. Not only did she not get better, her condition worsened being in small hotel rooms. She felt claustrophobic. She couldn't participate in any of the activities or do any sightseeing. Eventually, they cut short their holiday and returned home, distressed and disturbed. The home environment itself became fraught, because Rashmi would start yelling and screaming at the slightest disturbance. Even a phone ringing or the sound of the television would send her into a frenzy. She completely stopped communicating with her family members. She would not answer their questions or ask them any, and felt uncomfortable if anyone entered her room. She asked her husband to sleep in another bedroom. The family was devastated. No one knew what to do. Nearly five months had elapsed since she first experienced heartburn. Her specialist referred her to a psychiatrist, who immediately prescribed her antidepressants.

This was when Rashmi called me. She knew the outline of Anna's case history, and thought I could help her just as I had helped Anna. She was afraid of taking antidepressants, concerned that she might develop a lifelong dependency. Rashmi wanted to know if I could help her in any way, through meditation, Ayurveda, yoga, healing – anything. When I heard her voice, I knew she would be okay soon. You know how you have these gut instincts; I had one about Rashmi from the outset. I knew she would be fine and that antidepressants were not for her.

'Do you trust me?' I asked her in our first phone conversation.

'Of course. That's why I'm calling you.'

'Fine. Don't start with antidepressants then.'

'I'll do whatever you tell me, but will I be okay?' There was only sadness in her voice.

'Yes. Just follow what I say.'

I explained to her the yogic concept of three bodies and told her that we would work on all three simultaneously. To begin with, I asked her to completely avoid all dairy foods, wine, poultry and meat including seafood (she loved prawns).

'No tea, no coffee, no processed foods, no canned juices, no artificial sweeteners and absolutely no fizzy drinks other than sparkling water,' I told her.

'What if I feel like drinking something hot?' she asked. 'It's pretty cold here.'

'Drink honey, lemon and tulsi,' I said. 'And please be patient. It can take up to six months before any yogic exercise shows its full results,' I added.

'Six months?' she exclaimed. 'I'll die in six months, Swami. I need something quick.'

'Rashmi,' I said, 'none of the quick methods have worked on you, have they? If you can give me patience, I can give you results.'

I pacified her, saying that she would start to see some results within three to four weeks at the most. Getting on with the actual treatment (or healing, if you will), I explained to her some yogic postures (thanks to YouTube, I could just direct her to the appropriate videos) and told her to follow my dietary principles so that we could heal her physical body. For the subtle body, I shared a specific visualization and meditation she was to do for fifteen minutes twice each day. And for the causal body, 'I would do my bit,' I said to her. We agreed to touch base in two weeks' time.

Four days later, my phone rang. It was Rashmi.

'Swami!' she said, 'I haven't had any reflux or heartburn in the past four days. Not even once. What did you do? But I'm really scared, because I'm constantly worried it could come back at any moment. It's a terrible feeling. I still don't feel like talking to anyone at home. I still don't want to get out of bed, but this is the first time in months that I haven't had heartburn. Will I really be fully okay again?'

'Patience, Rashmi,' I said, 'Hold your horses. It's not even a week. Please just continue with the meditation and diet.'

'Please say it, please,' she said. 'Will I be fully well again?'

'Yes. We'll talk again in two weeks from now. Okay?'

'Yes, Swami. I will not bother you for the next two weeks.'

Another three days later she called me again to report that the heartburn had not returned. At the end of the call she promised that she would not call me for another two weeks. That didn't happen. She kept calling me twice a week, sometimes thrice.

Honestly though, I didn't mind, because I know how we can become childlike when things start to fall back in place, when life starts to look up again. Like a child, she had become at once excited and apprehensive. This happens in depression: you become a child. You start behaving like one – no rationale or logic seems to work for you. Thus, in some sense at least, a patient of depression should be dealt with in a similar manner in which we would deal with a child – with love, patience and a degree of tenderness.

In about two months, the nature of Rashmi's questions and the tone of her voice had changed. She was sounding happier in each subsequent phone call. 'You know, Swami,' she said one such time, 'last night we all went out for dinner. They didn't look like strangers any more. We laughed and we had good food. I ate outside after so long. I did not get any reflux. I invited my husband back to our bedroom for the first time in months.'

This was in 2007, and it's now 2015. Rashmi hasn't had any episode of heartburn or depression in all this time. She has remained a vegetarian and continues to meditate.

Once again though, as with Anna's case, meditation and diet were important in Rashmi's recovery; but what really healed her was love and care. Her family gave her the personal space she needed. Until she recovered fully, they tolerated her mood swings and understood that she was not well, that she wasn't behaving unreasonably with intent. Her husband's love perhaps played the most important role. When you hug someone; when you express love for her by giving her a simple peck on the cheek or holding hands, your systems release oxytocin – a happy chemical if you will – and levels of cortisol, a stress hormone, lower. A loving physical touch also helps the release of serotonin and dopamine, two other important neurotransmitters that add to your overall sense of well-being. When it comes to healing depression, a loving and supportive environment, a good diet and some physical exercise are just as important as medication.

The most important lesson I learnt from Rashmi's case was that depression can be confoundingly unpredictable. There may be risk factors, but there are no definitive criteria for succumbing to depression. Rashmi had lived by the book. Other than work, there were no major dramas or stresses or complicated designs in her life. She was a confident and successful woman who wasn't even overly ambitious. Tim's and Anna's tortured childhood years stood starkly remote to her pleasant and happy upbringing, yet although Rashmi's suffering in depression was relatively brief, it wasn't any less intense than Tim's or Anna's. Because depression is the sting of a scorpion, brevity does not diminish its intensity – it pains just as much.

Along with the intense pain that is experienced almost universally by sufferers of major depression, almost every patient feels alienated and detached from the world. If you have lost the taste for most things you enjoy, and you find yourself indecisive as well as indifferent – further, you feel cut off from your loved ones and indeed humanity and life – chances are you are suffering from such depression. This variety of the illness can be quickly and easily cured, provided it is properly diagnosed and acted upon; for when untended, most major depressive episodes worsen. It is imperative too, when major depression is triggered by a change in the physical world, that some corrective action is taken. For example, it could have resulted from a relationship break-up, the loss of a job or a promotion and so on and so forth. If some specific event has triggered your depression, it is best to work towards your fulfilment and keep the mind busy, or it will cling to that negative event and drag you down further.

Sometimes, strange as it may sound, depression is the body's way of telling you that certain things you've long been ignoring need your attention. Any event that triggers depression may thus be viewed as a wake-up call. If you don't wake up yourself, though, life will then wake you up the hard way.

You sit here for days saying,
This is strange business.
You're the strange business.
You have the energy of the sun in you,
but you keep knotting it up
at the base of your spine.
You're some weird kind of gold
that wants to stay melted in the furnace,
so you won't have to become coins.

– Rumi[7]

5

Leave Me Alone
Mild Depression

Life is hard work. I'm not even talking about paying your bills, staying debt-free, saving for a rainy day, keeping healthy, planning your retirement or making relationships work. That's nothing (just kidding). No doubt, these tasks make our lives challenging – and perhaps rewarding too. What I'm actually talking about though, is something quite simple: being happy. Whatever we do, and no matter how sincere our efforts, happiness continues to remain fleeting. It is an elusive state of being, like the lone cloud on a sunny day that appears but briefly, then disappears into the vast azure beyond.

For someone who hasn't found her purpose in life, or for someone who is not passionate about what he does, living can be a wearisome task. Happiness should be natural to us, because we are beings of joy; we are born out of love. Even the umbilical cord that nourishes us for nine months – the very connection with our mothers – is cut right at birth to mark our freedom. There are no strings attached.

We are happy, we are free. Or are we? Happiness should be natural to us, but it almost seems we have to constantly work towards it – we feel that we should catch the cloud and hold it in our grasp rather than just be as it is.

Sadness is a sneaky emotion. Just as no matter how well you feed yourself, hunger starts tugging at your stomach within a few hours, regardless of how happy you are, sadness – with or without its cousins: grief, anger, guilt, melancholy, resentment, fear, repentance etc., – quietly waits in ambush. You feel elated when you get a promotion; and the next moment the pressure at work starts. You feel euphoric when you buy a big house, and then the stress of meeting mortgage payments kicks in: 'What if tomorrow I don't have a job, how will I support my family, how will I pay my bills?' It is as if you thought happiness were your soulmate, but she turned out to be a courtesan instead.

Herbert Shipman famously said, 'Across the gateway of my heart I wrote, "No thoroughfare." But love came laughing by and cried, "I enter everywhere."' Perhaps the same can be said for sadness. In fact, the more you try to avoid or suppress your sadness, the longer it lingers in your heart. Mild depression is intense sadness that appears disproportionate and disordered. It can leave you reeling, along with your loved ones. It colours your whole experience of life like a dose of intense sadness.

Imagine that you are excited about your upcoming anniversary dinner. You have been planning it in your head for days, if not weeks. You've booked a table, you know which dress you are going to wear; you have the matching handbag and your new shoes – oh, the new shoes. You had saved up to buy those shoes for months. These are the very same shoes you had talked about once, and you have even showed him a picture that you had clicked of them at the mall.

Your partner comes home from work, half an hour late and steps into the shower while you are all ready and waiting to go. He dresses quickly and mechanically. You are hoping he'll notice your shoes any minute now or tell you how beautiful you look, but he doesn't. You sashay towards him, asking with an appealing smile, 'How do I look?' He says, 'You're looking very pretty,' but he seems distracted. You walk out with him, even more certain that he'll notice the heels now, but he doesn't. He tells you that he'll make a stop to fill the gas tank.

You begin to feel disconnected, and your anticipation is ebbing. He hasn't even noticed your handbag, much less your shoes. He doesn't really love me, you think. He's not the romantic type. He's just interested in his garage tools and car cleaning. As the moments pass, you become ever more melancholy. You start to ruminate on all the other times that he didn't notice you but was quick to notice everything else – notably, other women. An inner debate rages in the court of your mind. The defence declares, 'He's not bad, this is just how he is, look how caring he can be,' etc. But the prosecution is more persuasive: 'But how could he not notice the shoes? Shoes are important to you – he knows that. How could he be so insensitive?'

At dinner, the sublime ambience, food, wine and desserts have lost their appeal. You go through the motions, but it is a hollow commemoration of your relationship. You drive back home with him almost in silence. Even you don't like your shoes any more. And later if you confront him, you are sure he won't be able to understand your sadness. He will tell you that you are being oversensitive or that he can never please you; he will have a whole dialogue ready to assault your feelings. He may even say sorry afterward in a tone that betrays he doesn't really mean it. He will surely think you are overreacting.

By the time you arrive home, you are sure that one of you is going to start a discussion that can only end badly. You don't know what to say, but before you can think of anything, he broaches the topic. He apologizes for being remote and preoccupied. He tells you that a major deal he had been working on for months fell through today. He explains that he didn't want to spoil your anniversary dinner by telling you. Your sadness evaporates, and you feel more than a little foolish. He tells you that you are as beautiful as the day you met him, and your outfit is stunning. All is forgiven, and your anniversary evening is salvaged.

This sadness is disproportionate and irrational, but while depression is not just intense sadness, its sufferers can appear equally unreasoning. Someone in depression's thrall does not even know where their reactions are stemming from; they don't feel they are disproportionate, except perhaps upon later reflection. They don't want to feel hopeless or desolate, but it's not as if they are choosing to be this way. Depression is a disorder, a dysfunction that has gone well beyond a bout of sadness.

Sadness, though, can easily become depression when it chooses to stay in your mind longer than you can bear it. It no longer remains just sadness then – which may just be a temporary emotional state – it becomes depression, which is a lingering state of being. And just as you can feel you are possessed by a bout of intense sadness, depression can feel like a poltergeist is wreaking havoc inside you, controlling your very being. In reality, depression is usually the discontented ghost of past hurts – sadness that can no longer be contained in some recess of your mind – and it roams freely about your consciousness until you come to terms with it or until it is exorcised.

Sometimes, with the help of medication or certain conscious acts that you may find calming and fulfilling (like meditation, painting, praying etc.,) or less tangible factors (grace, nature, healing), the ghost of depression leaves you quickly. It doesn't haunt you for months or years as it did Tim or Anna, but departs within weeks. In the greater scheme of things, this is little more than a hiccup for your mental or emotional equilibrium. This is often the case with mild depression.

When mild depression hits you, though, you feel a pervasive disconnection from your world. You don't want to do anything or spend time with people, and you cease finding enjoyment in your favourite activities. Whereas mild depression is far from a severe major depressive episode, it is most often deeply disturbing and traumatic to you and your loved ones. In that feeling of distance and disconnection, you don't feel like socializing or even speaking to your own family. Others around you don't and can't understand your state of being. They try to talk to you; they worry for you. They try to make you feel better, but you push them away, sometimes bluntly, causing much hurt in the process. Your apparent indifference hurts them. They'll ask you repeatedly, 'What's wrong with you, why aren't you smiling, why aren't you being yourself?' and so on.

You want to say, 'Leave me alone.' Instead, out of courtesy, you'll simply say, 'I am tired.' You are not tired of living or doing things, you are tired of figuring things out. You are yourself surprised that you feel this way; you have no answer and the easiest response is 'I am tired,' so that others may leave you alone. But paradoxically, you don't want to be left alone. You want your loved ones' company, but you cannot handle having them around. You don't know what to do. The slightest dilemma leaves you overwhelmed, and you feel paralysed. Simple tasks like choosing what to wear in the morning or what you should eat for dinner seem daunting. Depression imposes a string of dichotomies, and you are no longer sure about anything.

A simple change in season, hormonal imbalances, a change in lifestyle, moving to a new place – even dietary changes can trigger depression. This form of depression is usually mild. The symptoms are generally limited to boredom, sluggishness, stupor, temporary insomnia, phobia and restlessness. Mild does not mean it is harmless, however. Its effect on you is profound. It's not like your best friend can arrive in good cheer and say, 'Let's go out for a coffee,' and suddenly you'll feel okay. Even if Brad Pitt or Angelina Jolie invited you over for a coffee, you wouldn't feel fine – or at least then, your happiness wouldn't last. Mild depression is only mild to the extent that its effects won't perhaps last as long, and it won't be as debilitating, as a major depressive episode.

A good many of us will suffer from mild depression at least at some time in our lives. Who doesn't have a storehouse of unpleasant memories, hurts and unprocessed sadness tucked away somewhere in his consciousness? A grey sky, pouring rain, being shut indoors and so on and so forth; all of that somehow has the ability to send the mind on a downward spiral. Vedic scriptures state that sunlight and happiness have an intrinsic relationship – maybe because sunlight means evolution, it means growth. The

Vedic way is to get up in the morning during sunrise and offer oblations to the sun. In some ancient Eastern cultures, people would sing eulogies to the sun as their first duty of the morning. Hundreds of millions of Indians still do this.

All plants live by the grace of sunlight, and animals thrive by it. Knowledge and wisdom are synonyms of light. There are many people who feel depressed during rainy times or winter, especially in countries in higher latitudes with daylight-saving time where it snows. Similarly, those with allergies can feel depressed when under the influence of the weather. Some even feel depressed and anxious in the summer months. This kind of depression is categorized as seasonal affective disorder (SAD). Most sufferers' moods lift as they approach spring or autumn. Your immune system and mental resilience are weakened when you are depressed, though. If something untoward happens while one is suffering from SAD, mild depression can easily last beyond the season and even snowball into a major depressive episode.

Patients with SAD are not the only ones prone to depression brought on by the normal cycles of life. In women, pre-menstrual syndrome (PMS) can cause mild depression. Post-partum depression (PPD) – also called post-natal depression – affects a fair number of women after childbirth to varying degrees. Throughout her pregnancy, an expectant mother endures pains, aches, morning sickness and all those invasive medical examinations and what not. She cannot eat half the things she craves, and she won't take paracetamol because it could affect the baby inside her. She spends every spare moment thinking about the arrival of her child. Finally, after nine long months, her child – her heart, her life – arrives in the world.

Not even a month passes though, before the mother starts to feel somewhat lost and sad. She may have already begun to feel a creeping melancholy ahead of the birth. Now, she is not tired of having put on weight; nor is she feeling left out when people around her go about their usual routine while she's left looking after the newborn. She is not tired of being awakened by the baby at ungodly hours, or even constantly nursing the child. Only a mother can truly understand that these new challenges are not making her tired, because her child means the world to her. But she's certainly tired. This is because she's left with no time for herself.

When you don't allow time for yourself, you can't receive the light in your life. It's like you are in a sunny place, but you have built a room around yourself with no windows or door. Light is abundant, but you can't enjoy it – you can't even perceive it, for the walls separate you from the light around you. Depression is disconnection. The more disconnected you feel from yourself, the more distant and stranger everyone else appears. The more you feel 'I don't know me', the more you feel 'I don't know you'.

In most ancient Eastern cultures, women's innate connection to the cycles of life was venerated, and much attention was accorded them at crucial times. Women were allowed time for complete rest during their periods, and they spent weeks, even months, with their parents for prenatal and post-natal care. Oestrogen levels are particularly low after childbirth. The rationale for an expectant mother being with her parents was that women are generally closer to their parents than parents-in-law. It was considered important for the health of both mother and child, when they are most vulnerable, to be in a loving, supportive and caring environment.

It is worth noting here that if your parents understand you and support you, there's practically nothing you lack. You can probably put down this book right now, hug your parents and spend time with them, and all will be well. But if you don't have that kind of rapport with them, then I suggest you don't try any such thing till you finish this book. And you think I'm kidding? Okay – maybe.

While support from family and loved ones is paramount for healing any kind of depression, we should be aware that when one is suffering from mild depression, even the least stress or minor mishap can catapult him into a major depressive episode. And though many cases of mild depression can seem to lift with time, understanding and therapy of some kind or the other, there are instances where more radical life changes are necessary to bring the light back into one's life.

This brings to mind Uday's experience. An Indian immigrant, Uday had been living in Toronto for nearly fifteen years and had recently got a big break with a Fortune 500 company in Washington. It was the type of opportunity that you can only dream of when you are in your final year at university. Uday's new job meant he would have the sort of office you fancy when you walk around the corridors of a corporation and secretly tell yourself, 'One day I'll be in an office like this, with views of the skyscrapers and my personal assistant just outside.'

It is hard to overstate Uday's achievement. The luxury of being able to shut your door to indicate you are not to be disturbed, the sheer sense of satisfaction you get when you flash a brief, artificial smile from inside your glass cabin to those walking outside – those working in cubicles of the size of municipal garbage bins – let me tell you, it's like nothing else. Getting to this level in the corporate world is no mean feat. Less than 3 per cent of the working population ever make it here. This is where Uday was going: a sumptuous corner office, high six-figure-salary package, a PA, a corporate credit card; and an annual budget of more than USD 1 billion.

Uday and I had been friends for years. He was an IIT graduate, had an IIM MBA and was only thirty-seven years old when he got this big role. A stellar career seemed assured for him.

Just a few months after Uday had assumed his new position, he called me in the middle of the night. At first I thought perhaps he didn't realize that while it was day in America, it was night in India – that he had miscalculated the time difference. But the tone of his voice quickly dismissed this thought; something definitely was not right.

Before I could ask him how he was doing or what the weather in Washington was like, he said, 'I'm really scared, Swami. My heart's thumping constantly. I'm dead meat.'

'What happened?' I was still emerging from my sleep.

'They handed me a notice of suspension,' he said, his reply almost overlapping my question.

'But, why? What did you do?' This was serious.

'I awarded a multimillion-dollar contract to a new vendor.'

'How can they suspend you just for that?'

'It's really complicated. I don't know what to do.'

'Talk to me.'

'What talk, Swami? God screwed me while I was bending down in reverence. I was just doing my job.'

'Uday!' I said, 'Just tell me what happened.'

'By some rotten coincidence one of the directors in the

vendor's company has the same surname as mine. And it's a small company.'

'That's not enough to suspend someone!'

'Swami, I'm being investigated for fraud,' he said without even hearing what I was saying. 'They could file criminal charges against me.'

'Okay, but did you do anything wrong? Tell me the truth.'

'How could you ask this question, Swami – you, of all people?' he exclaimed. 'Of course, I didn't do anything wrong.'

'Fine, then. You've nothing to worry about.'

'Nothing to worry about?' He was almost breathless. 'It was most humiliating, Swami. I was asked to surrender my blackberry, my ID and my laptop. I'm not allowed to speak to anyone at work or show up at the office until they conclude their investigation.'

'Did someone suspect you of wrongdoing or what? I mean, why did they not ask you first rather than start an investigation right away?'

'We have a bot (an automated system) that runs on the employee database and the vendor database, looking for patterns of fraud. It's by sheer coincidence that we shared the same surname and that I approved this vendor.'

'Uday, I need to ask this again and I need you to answer it clearly. You didn't do anything wrong, right?'

'No, Swami. I swear by God. There are no cuts or kickbacks if that's what you are asking. Not even a penny. Not even a free dinner. But I hired this vendor without an approval from the global sourcing team.'

'Shoot! That's a big mistake. How could you do that, you know? It's plain dumb and unnecessary.'

'Because these guys take forever to approve a vendor, especially if it's a start-up or a small company.'

'They have called the vendor for a separate meeting and asked them to produce all contracts, purchase orders, invoices, deliverables and project documentation,' he added. 'I feel like my heart's going to fly out of my chest. I am screwed in my head.'

'Okay, just take a breather,' I said. 'You have nothing to be afraid of.'

'But I'm so depressed. I felt so embarrassed, because this meeting took place in my own office and my PA was sitting outside. She saw that I was handing over my blackberry and ID, etcetera. To not make it too obvious, because the investigation is still going on, the head of HR escorted me out. I'm sure by now the whole floor knows the story. This will be the talk at lunchtime. How they'll love to mock me over beers. They must think I'm a fraud.'

'Let's not read into the situation. It'll only cause more anxiety. Is someone there to take care of you?'

'You know my whole family is in Toronto. That's the other thing – they are due to move here in six weeks' time. I've already signed a lease for a bigger apartment. School fees for the kids have been paid. The packers have been hired back home. And now this! Oh God, what do I do?'

I could not just sense his fear, I could hear it. He was barely pausing to draw breath; his words were staccato like a machine gun's chatter. He was in a terrible place. His voice conveyed such fear, anxiety, pain and shame, that for a moment, I even thought he had no chance. You have to understand I was dragged from my dreamland in the dead of night to have this conversation.

I tried to soothe him and steer him towards some

constructive thinking. 'Don't worry, Uday. It's important that you speak to the HR department or give them a written statement succinctly documenting your side of the story and the chronology of events.'

'Swami,' he said, his voice choking, 'I can't even imagine writing a document right now. I'm so messed up. I don't even know what I'm saying right now. What ...'

'Uday!' I intervened curtly. 'Stop it. Listen to me. We need to act.'

'I can't, I can't, Swami. I keep imagining what my colleagues must think. I'm not a crook. Even if I get a clean chit, how will I face them? What will I tell my wife?'

'Hey, take it easy, man. There are plenty of opportunities for sharp people like you.'

'Look where my sharpness has got me.'

'Uday, stop whining like a stray dog. Let's find a solution.'

'I'm totally broken, Swami. I am scared. I've locked myself in this apartment and I am scared to step out. What if I run into any of my colleagues?'

'Stop imagining things, Uday,' I said a little sternly. 'Are you going to act like a man or do you want to run away with your tail between your legs?'

'I want to run away, Swami,' he said gravely.

'Then I can't help you. Truth never runs away. Truth stands. It's the only thing that stands, for that matter. We are wasting each other's time. You decide how you want to be seen: a coward or a fighter, an honest man or a fraud. You know your truth, so act accordingly.'

'I've got my answer, Swami,' he murmured. 'I'm going to face the situation. What's the worst that can happen, after all?'

He agreed to face the situation, but it was a long walk home. He called me every day, sometimes twice a day. For an entire fourteen days, he still did not step out of his apartment. Pizza was the only thing he ate during this period. He would skip his breakfast, skip his lunch and call me late in his evening (which was my morning). After speaking for nearly an hour, he would order a pizza and send me an email saying he ate.

Two weeks later, he called me in the middle of the night again.

'I just finished my meeting with them,' he said.

'And?'

'They've dismissed me.'

'Oh, I'm really sorry, Uday. But don't worry, you'll find something else. I'm sure of it.'

'They said while I did not have any vested interest, bypassing the approval process did not suit a senior executive like me. It was a grave error, they said. My stock options too stand forfeited. They said they'll confirm my employment and salary to any future employer but they'll also state that I was terminated due to violating the operating procedures of the company.'

'That's really sad. But it's not the end of the world, you know.'

'I'm actually quite relieved, Swami,' he said. 'The last two weeks was the most devastating period of my life,' he added. 'I don't know what I'm going to do now. I'll go back to Toronto and see what I want to do next.'

Uday moved back to Toronto. What he went through in those two weeks, when he locked himself away from the world, wasn't really depression: it was distressing, it was painful; but it wasn't depression. Putting him on antidepressants would have been counterproductive, even damaging. Uday's story is not over yet, though.

Soon after moving back to Toronto, he started looking for jobs. But who would hire him with such a reference – and that too at the C-level? No one did. His credentials, his capabilities, his performance track record – nothing mattered. Eventually, Uday 'massaged' his résumé, erasing the Washington debacle and showing the gap as a sabbatical. Within a month, he was hired as a vice-president of Canada's top financial institution. This was one step down from his position in Washington, yet it was a lucrative job.

Everyone thought the worst was over. Professionally, maybe. But the inner storm had just begun to brew.

Uday called me after four weeks of working in his new position. 'I can't work,' he said. 'I don't feel like getting up in the morning. I can't sleep or concentrate. I feel this tightness at the back of my head all the time.' Like most under the spell of depression, Uday couldn't reconcile himself to his own feelings. 'The job, package, company, role – everything is great. I just don't feel like doing it,' he said. 'I don't understand it. I should be happy because I got a big break again, but I'm utterly sad and depressed.'

He had bills to pay, however, so he carried on with his work. Not for long, though. He worked for just under four months in his new job, a position that even he acknowledged was an excellent opportunity for him. This is where intense sadness differs from depression: depression does not respond to any rationale or logic. You can't reason it out. It's a condition, not a stance or perspective that you can just change. Uday could not convince himself to get to work just because he had a family to run. Depression had overtaken him. Like Tim and Rashmi, he stopped communicating, and he shut himself in his room.

Uday's inner wisdom told him that there was a deeper reason for his bout of the blues than merely the stress from his misadventure in Washington. 'I must quit,' he said. 'I can no longer see myself doing a nine-to-five job. I can't see myself doing anything at all, presently. I don't want to do this to my wife or kids, but I'm helpless. I feel like running away from the whole world. All these years have been a complete waste. I just feel tired all the time. No one gets it. They think I haven't recovered from the Washington incident, but it's got nothing to do with that. Maybe this is just my midlife crisis.' His wife tried to persuade him to wait for a bit longer before resigning; but he had already made up his mind.

He called me immediately after tendering his resignation and took the next available flight to India to see me in person. 'I'm feeling much better after quitting, Swami,' he said. 'I love gardening and I love architecture. I ended up becoming a technology executive because my parents wanted me to do engineering and all that. But right now, I don't know if I'm capable of doing anything. I'm thinking of selling everything in Canada and moving back to India and living off interest income.'

'That won't be a fulfilling life, Uday,' I said, 'because those who are capable can't sit contentedly on interest incomes. Besides, Canada is a good country for your children. Maybe you should do something related to architecture, gardening or something like that.'

'You think I can?'

'Why not?'

'It's not like I'm twenty years old. I've a family to feed, you know.'

I drew myself a bit closer and said, 'Uday, it's never too late to work towards what you find meaningful. Passion creates opportunities automatically; and purpose fulfils them effortlessly. It's far more gratifying to dance with your dreams than to be deprived of them.'

Uday chose to dance with his dreams. After spending a month in an Ayurvedic spa in Kerala, he went back to Toronto. He started his own company that bought run-down houses, restored them and sold them at a premium. Three years later, Uday was buying farmhouses, dividing the acreage, and after readying them over a couple of years, selling the houses and land at almost double the price. More than just profitable, this was an endeavour Uday thoroughly enjoyed. His days of personal crisis were far behind him now.

The first episode where Uday had locked himself in his room for fourteen days – when he couldn't sleep or eat properly, when he felt engulfed by fear and didn't communicate – was not depression. It was shock, trauma, sadness, despondency and sorrow – a gamut of debilitating emotions – but not depression. It did leave its mark on him, though, and perhaps sowed the seed of depression in his consciousness. His second crisis, however – after he had just secured his role as VP and when life was looking up again – was undoubtedly depression. It is best described as mild, because he overcame it quickly and took control of his life again without much ado. Nevertheless, for the time when he was held in depression's firm grasp, it wasn't any less painful or less intense for him than Anna's, Tim's or Rashmi's depression was for them.

At any rate, Uday had no need for medication or meditation; his depression wasn't severe. A break from his routine, a change of place, rejuvenation at an Ayurvedic spa and a sense of direction moving forward helped him overcome the condition. The same couldn't be said for Anna, Tim or Rashmi.

There are three points worth making here: First, there's no definitive or absolute cure for depression. Different things work for different people; and unfortunately, sometimes nothing seems to work. Second, when it comes to assessing the condition, we shouldn't rush to hasty conclusions. It is important to carefully observe the patient and examine the symptoms. Third, before you can even think about the cure, you need to understand the nature of a case of depression. The efficacy of any treatment is directly proportional to the accuracy of diagnosis. If ordinary sadness is treated with antidepressants or mood stabilizers, for instance, this will certainly harm the patient. Diagnoses of depression must take account for the general behavioural tendencies of pessimism and negativity and grief and sadness.

In the thought-provoking book *The Loss of Sadness*,[8] there is a vignette that illustrates the vital distinction between normal human emotions and depression:

> An eminent researcher presented a paper on women who he claimed were suffering from chronic depressive disorder. One woman with children had been abandoned by her husband and was facing an enormous and chronic challenge in dealing with her impoverished circumstances. Her symptoms of sadness, worry, sleeplessness, and so on were indeed severe. Then, the woman won a lottery, yielding her a considerable amount of money. Strikingly, her chronic symptoms disappeared, leading our colleague to doubt that she had ever had a genuine disorder but instead had been understandably distressed by the overwhelming challenges that faced her.

Many of those whom I meet purportedly suffering from depression are, in truth, not depressed to begin with. They are perhaps distressed, sad or fearful – like the woman in the story above. Once the underlying cause of the fear or sadness or distress is dealt with, the symptoms of 'depression' vanish. The following months are often engaged with managing the withdrawal symptoms after coming off medication. In short, just because you are feeling sad or overwhelmed does not mean that you are suffering from depression. Conversely, suffering depression does not always engender crippling sadness and the abandonment of usual activity. Identifying bona fide depression, or at least differentiating it from normal human emotions and responses, is a crucial matter of diagnosis. Because worse than failing to diagnose depression is misdiagnosing it.

Try and penetrate with our limited means the secrets of nature and you will find that, behind all the discernible laws and connections, there remains something subtle, intangible and inexplicable.

...

We are in the position of a little child entering a huge library filled with books in many languages. The child knows someone must have written those books. It does not know how. It does not understand the languages in which they are written. The child dimly suspects a mysterious order in the arrangement of the books but doesn't know what it is. That, it seems to me, is the attitude of even the most intelligent human being toward God. We see the universe marvellously arranged and obeying certain laws but only dimly understand these laws.

– Albert Einstein[9]

6

Messengers and Warriors
Neurotransmitters and Antidepressants

Once upon a time, there was a cave. Always dark and damp, it was deep and long. Every day it would look up at the sky, marvel at the sun's brightness and feel jealous. There is the sun, it would think, in full light and warmth, in the big, bright sky; and here I am, all murky and gloomy. Why did it have to be like this? Why couldn't I be like the sun?

'You are very lucky, O Sun,' the cave shouted out one day, 'you are enjoying the vast expanse. There's no darkness, only warmth and light.'

'I'm sure you must have something to keep you satisfied,' the sun said.

'I wish. I've nothing.'

'Look around, I'm sure you will find plenty to be happy about.'

'You can never understand the dark depths of my world,' the cave said dismally. 'There's absolutely nothing beautiful about my existence. It's just darkness.'

'This can't be,' the sun replied with conviction. 'Everything has beauty if you care to notice it.'

'It's easy to say that from up there. Come and see the darkness of my world.'

The sun agreed to visit the cave. As soon as it entered, the whole cave was illuminated – it became warm and bright. The sun's light penetrated every nook and corner of its space.

'Where's the darkness, O Cave,' the sun said finally, 'I don't see any.'

In Plato's *Euthyphro*, Socrates asks an interesting question, one that has been debated throughout the ages by countless wise souls, theologians and philosophers: 'Is an act pious because it's dear to gods or is it dear to gods because it's a pious act?' Do we experience suffering because happiness is absent, or are we happy because suffering is not there? Is light an absence of darkness or is darkness the absence of light?

The dualism of the cave and sun is the truth of everyone's life, just like night and day is a truth for our planet. Everything in life is relative to its polar opposite; all emotions and experiences are cast somewhere on a myriad of dualistic continuums: hot–cold, good–bad, light–dark, high–low, happiness–sorrow, fame–infamy, right–wrong, positive–negative and so on and so forth. If one within any of these pairs did not exist, the other would not exist, either. Any meaning or value one holds for us is consequent on the other.

Nevertheless, we are the sun. Our true nature is pure bliss and joy, it's light. I can walk into a dark room hiding a small lamp in my palms. As soon as I open my palms, the whole room will be bathed in its light. I can't do the reverse:

I can't hide a bit of darkness in my palms and walk into a well-lit room hoping to make it dark. Our suffering can't cover our light beyond a certain degree. We must step out of the cave though, for the more expansive our mind – our consciousness – the brighter we will shine.

In the Bhagavadgita, Krishna, a messenger of light and peace (also considered God by Hindus), instructs Arjuna on the battlefield when the latter, a warrior, feels unable to fight his own cousins. It is no coincidence that Krishna chooses to impart transcendental knowledge to Arjuna on the battlefield, because our lives are, in a way, battlefields. We are forever working with opposing forces within and without, and we are at times in earnest combat with our own tendencies. Sometimes, you will have to be a messenger of peace and at other times, you'll have to be a warrior; the fiercest engagements and the most significant truces you call, nonetheless, are of your inner world.

Even the human brain – perhaps the sole organ that bestows us humanity – is a battleground, with neurotransmitters engaged in endless back-and-forth battles. The human brain comprises neurons, which fire neurotransmitters to enable intercellular communication. Neurotransmitters can be broadly categorized into two types: inhibitory and excitatory. Excitatory neurotransmitters stimulate your brain, whereas the inhibitory neurotransmitters calm it. These opposing forces balance each other, allowing your proper functioning. It is when one of these becomes depleted – and the other gains the upper hand – that your equilibrium suffers.

For example, let's say you had an argument with your partner (this should be easy to visualize for most of us, I reckon). To maintain attentiveness and a degree of aggression, an excitatory neurotransmitter, acetylcholine, is released to stimulate you. During the argument, you find you are not getting anywhere; you feel as if you are talking to a wall. Before your frustration and aggression goes beyond a point of manageability, you break down and start crying. With that crying, your brain releases endorphins, another type of neurotransmitter, which makes you feel light and calm.

Other than functioning as perennial antagonists, neurotransmitters act as messengers. Virtually all functions of your body are governed by neurotransmitters, for they are the chemicals that communicate information throughout the body, and therefore affect every aspect of your physiology. Your sleep, focus, concentration, weight, mood – everything is affected by neurotransmitters. Any instruction your brain sends to your body, from telling your heart to beat to asking your stomach to digest, is conveyed via neurotransmitters. Think of your brain as the general post office and various neurotransmitters as postmasters delivering messages. Neurotransmitters perform a vital role in your existence, for while you may have the healthiest colon or the strongest heart, if your brain does not instruct them to act, they'll cease functioning.

Suffice it to say, a depleted level of one or a number of neurotransmitters has an adverse impact on every aspect of your existence – physical, mental and emotional. When your brain is overstimulated – that is, there is an excess of excitatory neurotransmitters – the inhibitory ones swing into action to restore balance and calm your brain. In doing so, just like armed forces in battle, they become depleted. Anything that stimulates your brain will ultimately have a negative impact on you in the long run because in order to tackle excitatory neurotransmitters, the brain has to produce inhibitory ones, and there's only so much it can produce. That is why all stimulants and drugs, be it the seemingly innocuous caffeine, the more illegal cocaine and a whole host of other substances, eventually create dependency and do damage.

The human brain has dozens of different neurotransmitters. The exact number is not known, but it is well over a hundred. The four major neurotransmitters that are linked to depression are dopamine, norepinephrine, epinephrine and serotonin. The other neurotransmitters that directly impact mental and emotional health are acetylcholine, GABA (gamma aminobutyric acid) and oxytocin. These boost mental well-being. Serotonin is linked to a sense of self-esteem. Among other things, it regulates sleep, learning and sexual behaviour. Low levels of serotonin can affect obsessions and compulsions.

Some of our most relished dietary indulgences can have an adverse effect on serotonin levels. Drinking coffee, or any of the numerous other beverages containing caffeine, stimulates the release of serotonin in your brain. If you consume it habitually and excessively, though, your serotonin levels become depleted. A deficiency of serotonin, which is usually accompanied by feelings of moodiness or anxiety, can lead to sugar cravings in some individuals. This is because eating sugary foods or even those high in carbohydrates triggers a temporary release of serotonin. Binge eating or the excessive consumption of sugary drinks or eating desserts becomes their coping mechanism, which is detrimental to anyone's health in the long term. Now you no longer wonder why that chocolate mousse or sticky date pudding tastes so nice with a hot cappuccino!

Dopamine is also involved here. It affects your span of attention, motivation and drive for pleasure and reward. Additionally, it affects your ability to deal with stress. Serotonin and dopamine have an intricate relationship. When serotonin levels get a temporary boost from the consumption of sugar, dopamine becomes an inhibitory neurotransmitter. Therefore, the high you feel after consuming sugar has a negative impact on your span of attention. You find it hard to concentrate for long periods and to overcome this, your brain sends a signal again impelling you to drink another coffee. Thus, your fairly mundane coffee habit can lead you on a perpetual roller-coaster ride of highs and lows in moods and neurotransmitters – and regular shuttling between Starbucks and cake shops.

Your proper mental and emotional functioning is dependent on the robust interaction of neurotransmitters, and a suitable diet is essential for this. An imbalance in one or more neurotransmitters can have a cogent effect on you, and a number of neurotransmitters have been shown to affect people's behaviour in a very specific manner. Indecisive people often have low levels of dopamine. Norepinephrine regulates alertness. Abnormalities of these neurotransmitters cause various mood, anxiety and emotional disorders. GABA is an inhibitory transmitter – it calms down neurons to check the rapid firing of neurochemicals. Serotonin and GABA directly counter depression. Acetylcholine aids in memory storage and recollection. When a patient can't get away from certain thoughts from the past, or fears that have either triggered depression or aggravated it, consuming foods rich in acetylcholine – such as almonds, blueberries, broccoli and brussel sprouts – can help.

The importance of a carefully calibrated diet can barely be overstated in healing depression. My primary focus in helping Rashmi was with the foods she ate, and a complete change in her dietary habits alone allowed her to resume a happy, healthy life.

NEUROTRANSMITTERS AND YOUR BODY

Your body possesses ingenious systems that allow it to maintain balance. If you simply follow the basics of a good, wholesome, organic diet and exercise, it almost invariably runs smoothly, like a finely tuned machine. Only our excesses upset the body's natural balancing mechanism, leading to oscillations that call for levelling with external aids or a special diet. Your body knows how much neurotransmitters it needs to produce. It is worth noting here that the most tragic consequence of taking antidepressants is that it interferes with your body's natural mechanisms, and slows down the organic production of neurotransmitters. Because of the excessive supply of serotonin through the pharmaceutical intervention of Prozac, for instance, your brain thinks it is getting enough serotonin. It thus reduces your body's natural production of this neurotransmitter. So ironically, if you are prescribed Prozac to boost your serotonin levels, Prozac will ultimately cause the serotonin in your system to be depleted.

This damaging interference with the body's natural functions is the main reason why I am no great proponent of antidepressants. Moreover, antidepressants can adversely affect metabolic processes of the body via receptors in the gastrointestinal and endocrine system. Having said that, there are many cases where antidepressants seem to be the only solution – or, at least, the only short-term solution.

I've already talked at some length about neurotransmitters, but let me share with you the most important information. It is perhaps the only thing you need to know about neurotransmitters. Here it is: The source of neurotransmitters is actually not your brain but your gastrointestinal tract. Neurotransmitters are endogenous chemicals made from amino acids and other nutrients, including vitamins and minerals, which derive from the food you eat. If your gastrointestinal tract is not functioning properly – or your diet is lacking in nutrition – your body may be unable to maintain levels of neurotransmitters required for efficient, healthy functioning. Furthermore, stress, poor living conditions, alcohol, sleep deprivation, caffeine, drugs, prescription and off-the-shelf medicines can all cause the depletion of neurotransmitters.

Ayurveda states that 95 per cent of all diseases in the body originate from the gastrointestinal tract. There are foods and yogic exercises that can strengthen, nourish and nurture your gastrointestinal system. They are outside the scope of this book, because it's not just a matter of eating something specific or doing a particular exercise to remain healthy. A certain degree of holistic understanding is required; I cover that in my book *The Wellness Sense*. For now, let me give you the summary. The health of your gastrointestinal system depends on your dietary habits, mental health and physical exercise. And the level of neurotransmitters in your brain is largely determined by the health you gain (or lose) by your diet and exercise.

While neurotransmitters are derived from nourishment in your diet, appropriate physical exercise is imperative for the proper functioning of the body. Moreover, physical exercise itself stimulates the production of serotonin. The joy experienced from engaging in an athletic activity or winning a match for example, can also give rise to increased activity in neurotransmitters in your brain.

By restoring the balance of neurotransmitters in your body, you can substantially lessen the impact of depression, anxiety, panic attacks, hypersomnia, insomnia, migraines, irregular appetite and bulimia. A moderate and suitable diet, exercise, rest and proper sleep are thus the finest methods for healing depression – free of any side effects that accompany the use of antidepressants. Later in this book, I elaborate on the various foods you can eat that boost your neurotransmitters.

I know what you might be saying now: when you are in the depths of major depression, you just don't have the motivation to do anything. You are unable to eat or sleep properly; you can't rest and you are barely fit for anything – even the most basic tasks feel arduous. In this state, maintaining a strict diet and exercise regime, and ensuring that you enjoy proper rest, is perhaps out of the question. This is where antidepressants come in.

THE CASE FOR ANTIDEPRESSANTS

We live in a world where more and more people are happy to pop pills or eat supplements to lose weight rather than sticking to the discipline of properly eating, sleeping and exercising – the three factors that have the greatest impact on gaining or losing weight. I'm not referring here to cases of pathological obesity. Similarly, there are many people who are sad or down because they are facing certain challenges in their lives, and a considerable proportion of these take anti-depressants. Most of these people could overcome their sadness or repair their broken-down state by leading healthier and more disciplined lives, but this requires effort and motivation, and sometimes a degree of enlightened direction from others.

We need to be more cautious in ascribing sadness and feelings of being overwhelmed by life to depression, when the catch-all treatment for depression is pharmaceutical intervention. It seems that the easy way out is to pop a pill and be over with it – if it were that simple. The result is an astounding proliferation of antidepressant use in recent times, which could hardly correspond with a similar increase in the incidence of depression. The sociologists Allan V. Horwitz and Jerome C. Wakefield offer some fairly shocking statistics in their book *The Loss of Sadness: How Psychiatry Transformed Normal Sorrow Into Depressive Disorder*:

> Although medication has been a common treatment for life problems since the 1950s, its use has undergone a staggering growth in recent years. Antidepressant medications, such as Prozac, Paxil, Zoloft, and Effexor, are now among the largest selling prescription drugs of any sort ... Their use among adults nearly tripled between 1988 and 2000 ... In any given month, 10 per cent of women and 4 per cent of men now use these drugs ... During the 1990s, spending for antidepressants increased by 600 per cent in the United States, exceeding $7 billion annually by the year 2000.[10]

In our fast-paced, stressful and distracted world, we want easy solutions; we want quick fixes. There is no doubt, however, that antidepressants can be very effective in treating a major depressive episode. They may be invaluable in helping to restore a certain normalcy in your life, so that you may work on more permanent solutions. Only in the most extreme cases, though, should anyone contemplate the use of antidepressants for protracted periods of time. So long as you keep in mind that in the long term, antidepressants are detrimental to your health and well-being, you have every reason to find a way to come off them.

We should also bear in mind that in a sense, taking antidepressants is not too dissimilar to snorting cocaine, for this also triggers the release of mood-altering neurotransmitters. Loren Parsons, an assistant professor in the Department of Neuropharmacology at The Scripps Research Institute (TSRI), confirms that 'When ethanol [alcohol], cannabinoids [marijuana], opioids [opium, heroin] or psychostimulants ['chalk' or crystal meth] are taken into the body, serotonin levels in the brain are elevated.' Significantly, he adds, 'This elevation in serotonin plays a role in the motivation to continue taking drugs.'[11]

Just like using illicit drugs, taking most antidepressants flushes your brain with an artificial level of neurotransmitters. (Though SSRIs, or Selective Serotonin Re-uptake Inhibitors which are a class of drugs that are often used as antidepressants in the treatment of depressive and anxiety disorders, don't actively flush the brain with serotonin themselves, but interfere with the scavenging effect, which in turn facilitates the raising of serotonin levels.) Your brain mistakes this for an organically created reserve of the neurotransmitters. Intoxicants – whether they are euphoria-inducing narcotics (opium, heroin, morphine), soporific hypnotics (benzodiazepines or sleeping pills), perception altering hallucinogens (LSD, marijuana), energizing stimulants (cocaine – and even caffeine) or stupefying inebriants (alcohol) – all work, in some way, like various antidepressants, tranquilizers or mood stabilizers. They may artificially boost the production of neurotransmitters or they may imitate a receptor or block it altogether.

One of the more common recreational drugs, ecstasy (methylenedioxymethamphetamine or MDMA), causes production of serotonin, but when taken in excess it damages the nerve cells using serotonin. This itself leads to depression. Antidepressants can similarly alter the brain's functioning such that without their support, you will be more prone to depression than you were prior to their use. In simple terms, all of these chemicals – of the illicit or prescription kind – trick your brain and inhibit its ability to produce mood-stabilizing neurotransmitters naturally. Antidepressant use can thus lead to physical dependency, just as the use of these other chemicals can. There is a biological, emotional, mental and financial cost attached to antidepressants which is often overlooked by those who prescribe them and those who use them.

I do not wish to disregard antidepressants' usefulness, because they do help a remarkable number of patients. When depression is truly depression – clinical or pathological – where it has gone far beyond sadness or trauma and has taken on a life of its own – they can be invaluable in restoring some semblance of normality to a patient's life. But we shouldn't stop there. What happens if you visit a doctor and find out that you have diabetes? She will give you medication; but she will also tell you to take care of your diet, to go for long walks and so on. Medication alone will not help you combat diabetes. Similarly, antidepressants are only designed to assist you in overcoming depression. They are no panacea; the best you should hope for is that you feel somewhat normal till their chemical action fades.

Their purpose should be to stabilize your condition so that you can set the pace and take control of your life, and move towards a point where your brain will no longer require medication. You should take them with the intent that you will not need them after a point.

If your neurotransmitter levels are alarmingly low due to poor diet and lifestyle, even antidepressants can't help you much, because they need neurotransmitters to work with. Moreover, artificially replenishing neurotransmitters with antidepressants can cause headaches, a dry mouth, insomnia, irregular or hard bowel movements, constipation, nausea and bruxism (teeth-grinding). These are just some of the side effects of antidepressants. For more, simply open the information leaflet supplied with an antidepressant and go through it. The benefits are summed up in a line or two, whereas the side effects run into paragraphs.

Sedatives and sleeping pills are no different. Regular and prolonged use of sleeping pills, a form of intoxicant, also makes you more prone to depression. The rule of thumb is that any artificial chemical will have some impact on your brain. The point I'm making here is that antidepressants are legitimate medicines, but if you take them without finding a way to stop taking them, you'll ultimately do yourself more harm than good. Just like there's medication for high blood pressure, there's medication for depression. An enlightened approach to your well-being through diet, exercise and lifestyle – coupled with a healthy approach to life – can often cure both.

As there are many perspectives,
There can be many answers.
Yet, in the end,
The best answer to 'Why?' is
Why not?

We are afloat in
The Great River.
All are carried along.
Some swim against the flow.
They, too, are carried along.

The departure from what is natural is
The birthplace of personality.
The world of persons is
A solitary place,
Each separate and alone.
To achieve peace,
One must retrace the way one came.

– Wu Hsin[12]

7

Footprints of Time
Psychic Imprints and Your Mood

Once upon a time, there lived an angry man. He had been married for two decades, yet he didn't get along with his wife. He habitually fought with her for no real reason. He accused her of not being understanding. Deep somewhere though, he knew he wasn't being just; but he would get worked up over trivial matters and when he was angry, he would say and do things he would later regret. He hated himself for this. But no matter how hard he tried, he couldn't overcome his anger.

One day he approached his guru and said, 'I'm sick and tired of being angry all the time. Tiny matters set me off, and the fiend in me comes out without any warning. Why am I eternally angry and upset?'

'Because you are hurt,' the guru said.

'But I have a caring family and I love my wife. She doesn't hurt me back when I'm upset. So I don't think I'm hurt.'

'You are still experiencing the pain of old wounds. These

are the after-effects of what you may have experienced in your childhood or during your youth.'

'Have I not been healed all these years?'

'Not only have you not healed yet, but the hurt and the pain has made you weak. As a result, regardless of how pleasant or unpleasant the situation may be, any undesirable thought or emotion triggers the anger in you,' the master said calmly. 'A fit of rage is a sign of being hurt and weak.'

'I find it strange,' the man replied in disbelief. 'No one has duped me, I am a successful man. I don't remember anything major; maybe only small incidents have caused me pain. How can such experiences of the distant past still leave me weak, hurt and angry?'

The guru handed him his water pot and instructed him to keep his arm stretched while holding it.

'Is it heavy?' he asked.

'Not really.'

A minute passed and he asked the same question.

'It feels a little heavier now,' the disciple said.

'Stay put till I say otherwise.'

'My arm's aching,' he said after five minutes. 'I can't hold it any longer.'

The guru took the water pot from him and said, 'You see, it's not how much the water pot weighed but how long you carried it. The longer you hold it, the heavier it feels. Gradually, you feel weaker and weaker before you find it unbearable.'

While the gravity of a hurt matters, what matters much more is how long you've been carrying it. I frequently meet people who are in their fifties, sixties or even seventies, who have been married for decades, yet they complain about incidents that occurred thirty years ago as if they happened yesterday. These range from something as insignificant as not being served the right meal at their wedding to being lied to about something serious.

Every moment of every day of our lives unfolds a new experience. It's impossible to have only pleasant experiences, because what we experience is largely dependent on how we are feeling internally, rather than the absoluteness of the external condition itself. It is impossible to have only agreeable conversations with your loved ones. It's inevitable that there are going to be times when those closest to you will make mistakes or you will do so; there are times when you will feel that they don't understand you or they will feel that you don't understand them. It doesn't mean that your relationships are not workable or that there is no compatibility. Sometimes, it simply means that you've been carrying the water pot for a little too long.

Everything that you go through in your life – no matter how major or minuscule – leaves an imprint on your consciousness. Some imprints are like lines drawn on the surface of still water – they last only for a few seconds – and some are like lines drawn on sand. Lines on sand, however deep, are erased with the passage of time, when the next storm comes or by the changing tides of life. Sometimes you are healed of your past when a wave of happiness washes away your pain; and sometimes when you are engulfed by an overwhelming difficulty, you all but forget about life's smaller challenges. Most of life's events are like lines on the sand; they are ephemeral. They may cause pain, but when something momentous happens, they cease to matter.

Some experiences, though, are like lines scored on the surface of rock. They remain for an eternity. Imagine pouring water on to an unblemished slab of stone. The water will move freely across it. Imagine that the same slab has grooves etched deeply into its surface. Water poured on the slab will ineluctably channel itself in these grooves. Similarly, painful experiences leave an impression on your psyche like grooves in rock. The grooves become our coping mechanisms. They help us make sense of our world. When we experience anything, at first it travels through these neural pathways (grooves in the rock) we have created over the years.

Because our ways are so set, habits can be hard to break or develop. But you can create new neural pathways; it only takes six weeks. If you repeat a behaviour for this length of time, it will start to come naturally to you. It's like making a groove, deeper and wider than the others on the slab of stone. Any flow of water will now naturally flow in the new grooves. These are the imprints you create on your being: they can be carved into your consciousness as acts of volition, just as they are slowly worn by trudging the same old unthinking habits. Depression that lingers for any length of time can also wear its own groove, and you can become stuck, just as you would with any other habit.

More than medication, you need to create new, happier and more functional imprints to follow when a depressed state of mind becomes a habit. Sometimes, depression is labelled a mood disorder. This means little beyond the formality of a name. Your moods won't just swing on their own without any stimulus. Depression originates in the causal body, and the mind becomes a victim of its own latent tendencies. Thus, when you ignore your calling or persist in leading a meaningless life, you are courting depression. Many people lead unfulfilling lives; some choose to ignore the voice of the soul, whereas many others drown it out with the noise of empty activity. But one day, it all catches up with you. There can be no external medication for the sick causal body. Long before signs of depression show in the physical body, they have already fully manifested in the subtle body – in your emotional body, if you will.

Life is an aggregate of ceaselessly unfolding moments, a potpourri of experiences; an unmodified collection of psychic imprints that have been travelling with you, over lifetimes, making you who you are. This is evolution. Often a person may solemnly vow to do something – to form a habit, to carry out a plan, to meditate, to exercise – but somewhere between his resolve and execution, he loses motivation. People want to be disciplined – they even try hard to break their patterns – yet they often end up doing the very reverse of what they had sincerely intended. Does this mean their goals were overly ambitious, or that they were simply not serious enough in the first place? Not necessarily.

In the *Yoga Sutras*, Patanjali states that memory, a function of consciousness, is the unaltered collection of words and experiences. Whatever we hear or experience leaves an imprint on our minds. Some imprints engender peace and happiness, and some others cause grief and pain. You naturally aspire to a calm and balanced being, free from emotional disturbances. There are, however, memories that haunt you, traumas you cannot get over, people you cannot forgive, and so forth. You want to forgive or forget; you want to move on, yet, despite your best efforts, something rooted deep inside you stops you from expressing the joy within yourself. The culprit is the undesirable imprints, which are the primary triggers and storehouses of emotional afflictions.

This brings to mind Bo's experience. Bo was a high-level executive in his mid-forties, working for a large organization. Even though he had a happy family with a loving wife and two children, he was often battered by episodes of shooting pain in his right knee and wild mood swings. He was physically fit, and all his medical reports were fine. Nothing could explain his knee ache. As for the mood swings, they happened even when he was on a vacation, when there was no stress of work. To make matters worse, he experienced them more in a public setting. Moreover, Bo often said things that hurt his wife and damaged their relationship when he was in the grip of one of these episodes. He would later apologize but his apology would barely register, for the pattern of verbal bashing and subsequent apologizing seemed intertwined and constant.

Bo and his wife tried many things, without success. One day, they came across a certain therapist. He advised Bo to recall and narrate the major incidents of his life, especially those where he experienced grief and pain, physical or mental. A few sittings later, they figured out the cause of his sudden feeling of physical pain and wild mood swings. It turned out that Bo was bullied in school. One particular time, a bully gave him a nasty blow on his right knee with a baseball bat. The blow did not break his knee, but the excruciating pain from the blow caused him to scream uncontrollably. This immediately got the attention of his teachers, and he was promptly given medical aid. The bully was expelled from the school, and no one ever pestered him thereafter. It seemed that this horrible phase of Bo's life was over.

That experience, however, found a home deep in Bo's mind. Whenever he passed through markets, if he saw a baseball bat or even any memorabilia linked to baseball, he experienced pain in his knee. All this was happening in his subconscious mind; he was quite unaware of the source of his distress – at least consciously. Shouting became his coping mechanism, because this is exactly what he had done when he was hit by the bully. His mood swings were triggered by the sight of anything linked to baseball, especially the bat. With some awareness and therapy, Bo was able to all but erase the imprint his traumatic childhood event had left on his psyche, and hence free himself from these involuntary reactions.

You should be aware of the psychic imprints your life experiences have left on you. These imprints conjure up your thoughts, chart your tendencies, your habits, your nature and almost everything about you. This is why abusive relationships can be so damaging. They don't just destroy your self-esteem: the imprints left by them are those of a powerful habit, and can be deleterious to every aspect of your being. It is thus paramount that you take care of yourself. Love, empathy and care can heal even the most painful imprints, and manifesting these within yourself and for yourself is crucial to a healthy existence. I have known many people who have persisted in ignoring their own needs. They have dragged themselves through virtually every moment of barren, unfulfilled lives; but almost all of them have fallen victim to some disease or the other.

When you are not living a fulfilling life; when you are forced to accept something against your values; when someone tries to instil fear in you – or all of these – it is important to protect yourself. You should confront these people and situations; if confrontation is not possible, you need to distance yourself – and if you can't distance yourself, you surely must protect yourself. If you ignore your predicament, it will come back to haunt you in manifold ways – especially if you were the soft target or an innocent victim. When you remain quiescent in abuse, you only encourage the oppressor. Furthermore, the imprints of the abuse may well revisit you in the form of depression.

Monica's plight is a case in point here. A sensitive, erudite lady in her mid-thirties, Monica visited me a number of years ago. She was a highly regarded research scientist, and she had worked in a prestigious European academic institution where she had previously completed her PhD. whereas she was the soft and vulnerable type, her boss at the institution was the epitome of ego and vanity; and he vented his misogynistic spleen on Monica. She was a new recruit and he was a senior professor, and he subjected Monica to endless verbal harassment. Seeing that she was the quiet type – and that her boss was not a fan of her anyway – the whole work team became unsympathetic towards her.

Her boss would comment negatively on her dress sense, her hairstyle or even her spectacles, and her colleagues would join in. Their conduct could very easily have been deemed sexual harassment, but she had held little hope that anyone would support her if she had taken action against them. Monica would later recount that she didn't want her career to be jeopardized by complaining, because the field of academia is a very small world. Ultimately, her workplace became so unbearably stressful for her that she quit her job. She migrated to a different country altogether so that she could start afresh.

A good deal of damage had already been done to her, though, and Monica spiralled into what appeared to be a major depressive episode. She even developed suicidal thoughts. Her therapist prescribed a succession of different antidepressants in the hope that one of them would work, to no avail. She had a three-year-old son and a very caring husband, yet her husband's love and her child's smile couldn't bring her respite. With each passing day, her suicidal ideation only became stronger and depression's hold more debilitating. And a most worrying fear began to overtake her: the fear that she might harm her own child or kill herself. Monica found it hard to resist the suicidal allure of high-rise buildings. She was even afraid to see knives, because at the very sight of a knife she imagined herself doing something terrible with it.

In a rare move, I advised Monica to cease taking antidepressants completely. We then only focused on a certain meditation that would help her to erase the painful feelings from the many incidents at her workplace. This was because I didn't see her condition as depression, and I therefore didn't see the wisdom in trying to treat her with medication for an illness she didn't have. In my view, she was no more than deeply hurt and shocked. She was hurt because she had been ridiculed for her appearance and other personal matters, where only her competence and professional conduct should have mattered. She was shocked because she didn't think that in this day and age, she would ever have to endure such behaviour. The episodes at work had truly ravaged her self-esteem.

I asked Monica to do a certain intense meditation and go through a visualization of healing and forgiveness. Less than a week later (yes, only one week), she returned to Europe a happy woman. While she was initially a little apprehensive, negative thoughts no longer overpowered her, and she never touched antidepressants again.

Monica felt this was nothing short of a miracle. A month

later, when all was still well and she was finally convinced that she was cured, Monica got in touch with me again, and asked how this had been possible. She told me that she had applied all her knowledge and skill as a biochemist over a period of two years, researching and trying every known medication. She had scoured the Internet for the latest research on mental disorders and pored over countless academic papers, looking for some clue that could help her. All her efforts to rid herself of depression, nonetheless, had been in vain; she had even at one time become convinced that death was the only answer to her illness. She was, to be sure, overjoyed by her recovery; but its swiftness left her more than a little nonplussed. 'How come I felt perfectly fine within just one week?' she asked me.

'You didn't have any depression to begin with,' I said. 'You were just deeply hurt and you were carrying a lot of anger against your boss. I simply helped you to drop your baggage and move on with your life. Antidepressants had no role in this.'

'But I remember in our third meeting you touched my forehead and said, "From this moment on, negative thoughts will not overpower you," and after that day it's true, I never had the same thought upon seeing a knife. I never thought of suicide again. How is this possible?'

'Faith and consciousness,' I replied. 'Faith opens those doors to your consciousness that you didn't even know existed. My touch was simply a matter of transference. It was syncing your frequency with mine. Had you not been meditating, I couldn't have done that. Any more words and it'll be like my trying to explain why sugar tastes sweet.'

And that's the thing: meditation makes it possible for you to champion your own mind and emotions. It helps you to rid yourself of thoughts you don't wish to entertain. It is your portal to super consciousness – a state of your own being that transcends all fears and phobias. Meditation enables you to explore the uncharted territories of your universe-like consciousness. In this expansive space, you fly free like a bird in the azure sky, leaving behind no trail. Streams of peace and bliss flow like rivers after rains through a verdant, fecund land. All you experience is happiness, because your energies are aligned with your emotions and your thoughts are in harmony with your actions. There, the darkness of depression simply cannot coexist with the infinite light of your being.

Tell me, O Swan, your ancient tale.
From what land do you come, O Swan?
to what shore will you fly?

Where would you take your rest, O Swan,
and what do you seek?

Even this morning,
O Swan, awake, arise, follow me!
There is a land where no doubt
nor sorrow have rule:
where the terror of Death is no more.

There the woods of spring are a-bloom,
and the fragrant scent
'He is I' is borne on the wind:
There the bee of the heart is deeply immersed,
and desires no other joy.

– Kabir[13]

8

Show Me Light
Cure

In days of yore, tens of thousands of years ago, when lives were simpler – when learned priests would begin the day with Vedic chants, and people would awake to the dulcet singing of birds in the mornings or the sound of temple bells welcoming the divinity in the new day – there ruled a noble and a pious king. The king held sway over a mighty empire and was loved by his subjects; but he was completely untouched by pride or vanity. His life, though, was not complete. Nature had given him everything except one thing: a child, an heir.

Three queens graced his side. None, however, could bear him a child. The years had bestowed unimaginable wealth and fame upon him; but all that was of little interest to him, for his heart longed for a son. While the sun seemed to shine for him, and for all the illumination of the palace, his inner world remained dark and hopeless. The soft mattresses, exquisite delicacies, enchanting courtesans and overflowing coffers of the treasury – even the playful time with his queens – no longer held any pleasure.

Each passing day only brought more sadness for the king. He did yajnas, prayed, fasted, approached physicians and tantriks of repute and consulted wise men, but nothing could help him. One day, though, he heard of a great rishi who had descended from the Himalayas and established a hermitage in his kingdom. This was not just any sage but a true siddha who grants wishes – one who could peer into the future and manifest anything within the range of human consciousness and beyond.

The king went to the rishi with great hope and offerings. He was mesmerized with the radiant face of the sage; the rishi's piercing eyes, his still stature and speech would almost lead one to believe that he possessed the universe within his soul. The sage foretold that another queen, the fourth, queen will bear the king a child. The king thus hurriedly married the princess of a nearby kingdom and exactly as predicted by the sage, the new queen became pregnant. The king spent every moment of every day in great anticipation. Dozens of maids were retained to tend to the young queen's every need. Royal physicians stood at her beck and call. Nine months later, she gave birth to a beautiful child. The soft cries of the child not only broke the sombre silence of the palace, but also the hard shell of the king's sadness.

The midwife came running out of the labour room and said to the king, 'All glories to you, O King! The queen has given birth to a healthy and beautiful daughter.'

For a moment, the king thought that God had played some cruel joke on him. He wanted an heir – a valiant son who would conquer the world – and not a fragile daughter who would play with dolls. Meanwhile, the royal maids brought the newborn princess outside to present to the king. As soon as he held her in his arms, a stream of ecstasy, of unsurpassed joy, coursed through his entire being. He forgot all about his ambitions: looking at the fair face of the newborn, his own daughter, he felt his world was complete. Just as from a dark cocoon emerges a colourful butterfly that flits about fragrant flowers, the king's zest for life rose from the depths of melancholy. He had found a new world, and he began doting on the little princess – his everything. She's going to be the greatest and happiest person to walk on this planet, he thought.

The princess grew up to be a beautiful young woman of grace and intelligence. Tutors of renown from all over the world schooled her in music, painting, dance and every other skill befitting royalty, including the way of the warrior. The king even had her trained in Vedic chants and taught her every tradition. He was intent that she have the finest samskara (imprints of her experiences), all out of profound love. Indeed, he loved her more than anything or anyone else he had ever loved. He wouldn't have a meal without his beloved princess by his side. He wouldn't go to bed at night until he put her to sleep, stroking her fine and long hair, as dark as the night itself. Tales of the princess's beauty and wit soon started attracting proposals from the neighbouring kingdoms, but the king rejected them all. No one, he felt, was good enough for his precious child.

The king's heart would ache thinking that his daughter would soon leave him and live elsewhere. To take his mind off his fears, his queens suggested they spend a few days in the wilderness. The king felt that since his daughter might be married soon, he would not have such an opportunity again, so he readily agreed to the excursion. For her part, the princess was excited. Time in the woods seemed like an adventure after regimented palace life, and she gathered her entourage of attendants to be at her service. A large retinue carried tents, delicacies, musical instruments, the finest wine and everything else they could possibly want.

A suitable campsite was selected near a pond, where lotuses elegantly bloomed. A gentle breeze fanned the glade; young trees swayed gently nearby and the older ones stood majestically above. Horses and elephants were tethered, tents were erected and guards were deployed. The king stepped into the pond with his queens to sport in the water while the royal cooks got to work. Entranced by nature's beauty, the young princess ventured out to explore the woods with her handmaids and guards in tow.

As she wandered deeper into the forest, she came across a clearing that was strangely calm. The birds were quiet, deer were sitting nearby peacefully, and at a distance sat a couple of lions, docile and as tame as cows. Much to their surprise, no one felt any fear at seeing these big cats. The princess gestured the guards not to combat the animals, to let them be. The place was at once divine and earthly. Something then caught her attention. It was an anthill, larger than the usual size, about four feet high; and there were two glowing holes in it.

Thinking it was a sprinkle of fireflies, she went closer to examine the holes. Immense light was emanating from them, and she was transfixed for a moment. These couldn't just be fireflies, she thought. Intrigued, she picked up a dry stick lying nearby and thrust it into one of the holes. The whole anthill shook. Even more curious now, she probed the depths of the second hole, and a deafening howl reverberated through the woods. The deer fled from the scene and the lions too. The princess now saw what she had failed to notice after she had pushed the stick into the first hole: the end of the stick was smeared with blood.

She threw the stick on the ground and hurriedly left the place. Behind her, the anthill shook, crumbled and broke apart, and out stepped a sage. He had been meditating at this spot for years in such stillness that ants had made a hill around his body. He cried in pain as he cupped his bloody eyes with his palms. With his divine vision, he saw that the princess had blinded him. With an occult mudra, he released a fearsome energy in the woods that made the king and his queens go pale. They immediately lost their energy and appetite, and were stricken with such lethargy they were all but crippled.

Seeing her father's and the queens' suffering, the princess narrated what had transpired earlier. The king immediately ordered to be taken to the sage, along with his queens and the princess. He beheld the injured sage with horror as blood oozed from his eyes: this was Chyavan Rishi, the very sage who had blessed the king with a child years earlier. The king fell at his feet, begging Chyavan Rishi's forgiveness.

'I'm an old man, O King,' the rishi said. 'I've gone blind now. Who will take care of me?'

'I'll arrange for everything, Guruji,' the king replied. 'My personal servants will be assigned to look after you.'

'A paid servant is paid, after all, O King. They'll never have the same devotion. You must give me your daughter's hand, and she must look after me.'

The king was dumbfounded; he felt dazed, as if someone had hit him on his temples with a hammer. How can I possibly give my young and beautiful daughter to an old sage, who's blind too? How can I hand dawn to the hands of dusk? he thought. But he also knew that this was no ordinary rishi: he could destroy the king and his entire kingdom with the mere power of his mind.

'Please forgive my daughter,' he pleaded. 'Her whole life is ahead of her. I'll personally come and serve you.'

'No, great king,' the sage said firmly. 'It's not you but your daughter who bears this karma, so she must pay for it.'

'But, sage ...'

'No father, the learned rishi is right,' said the princess gravely as she stepped forward. She knew that the wrath of the sage would raze everything and everyone in her father's kingdom – the king included. She felt equally sorry for blinding a tapasvin; but beyond this, she saw within the sage's aged frame a fire kindled by austerities and penance, and it shone from every pore of his body. She felt irresistibly and inexplicably drawn to the rishi, like a moth attracted to flames. To assure the welfare of her father and repent for hurting the rishi – and to assuage her heart's yearning – she accepted him as her husband.

'I've hurt the noble sage, and I must redeem myself,' she added. 'I want to serve the rishi and be his wife, as is his wish.'

The king stood rooted to the spot, as if struck by lightning. He was quiet for a few moments and then indicated his reluctant assent with a desolate nod. He offered to provide every comfort for his daughter and the rishi in the woods.

'No father,' the princess said. 'Like a good wife, I must be happy with whatever my husband has. I'll gladly make do with whatever we have here.'

She took off her jewellery, touched her parents' feet and led the blind sage to his hermitage, which looked deserted since he had been in meditation for years. The queens' illnesses vanished and they promptly regained their vigour, but the king was devastated.

Vishada, depression, got the worse of him and he lost all interest in the affairs of the state, in his own well-being – and everything else. His very lifeblood seemed at an ebb. He no longer laughed heartily or slept with his queens. Wine didn't interest him; nor did dance and music. He would send entertainers away without even seeing their performances, and as time passed, his condition worsened. He felt responsible for his daughter's condition. Had he not camped in the woods on that fateful day, his daughter wouldn't be deprived of her royalty, he lamented.

As if his regret were not enough of a burden, the pangs of separation pierced his heart like poisoned arrows. Unable to bear his torment, the king went to the rishi's ashram. He saw his daughter sweeping the floor with contentment and serenity on her face. Sad and dazed, he approached the sage and offered his obeisance.

'I have not come to you as a father, O rishi,' he said. 'I have not come to you as a king either. I have come to you as a seeker.'

The sage nodded his old but wise head, his white beard touching his chest, his matted locks flowing freely like roots of a banyan tree.

'I've accepted that my daughter won't be a queen but the wife of an effulgent sage like you,' he said as softly and humbly as one should with the wise. But within, his heart seethed with resentment. This was never the fate he had envisaged for his royal princess. 'Why am I still depressed, though? I feel there's nothing left to live for,' he asked.

'You are depressed because you haven't yet come to

terms with the truth that all the dreams and desires you had for your daughter will never be fulfilled. It is your clinging to expectations that is causing you misery.'

'But is it wrong for a father to have these desires?'

'It's not about right or wrong. Desires are just that – desires. No one has ever gained eternal happiness by chasing their desires, for they are endless.'

'With due respect, my only desire was that I wanted a royal family for my daughter, a life filled with comfort and riches.'

'That is an illusion, O King! You not only wanted a royal family, you wanted a caring husband for her, a strapping youth, someone who would love her, provide for her and look after her. You wanted them to have a royal heir who would be equally if not even more capable than yourself. You wanted their glory to never fade away. At the same time, you also wanted a life free from calamity. And even if nature were to grant you all this, you would then want to expand your kingdom; you would have embarked on campaigns of conquest, subjugating other states and on and on and on. It is never ending. Desires exist in the human mind like limitless air in the sky. And they are the root cause of all emotional and mental turmoil. Give up your desires and vishada will leave you immediately.'

'Why can't I be happy by fulfilling my desires?'

'Seeking happiness by fulfilling desires is like a dog trying to catch its own tail. The laws of the universe are outside the comprehension of human consciousness. Play along.'

The king bowed before the sage and set out for his palace, a little wiser, but nevertheless just as dismayed as before.

Months passed, and Chyavan Rishi recovered his youth and sight by virtue of his penance and a boon from the

Ashwini Kumar twins, the physicians of the gods. With the power of his tapas, he transformed his hermitage into a heavenly place, rich and complete in every aspect. The wife of the sage experienced every joy known to a woman.

Many times the sun rose and many times it set; days, weeks and seasons passed. The king missed his daughter – he longed for a mere glimpse of her, but he couldn't bear to see her sweeping floors in a remote ashram. One day he could resist no longer and decided he must see his princess, the apple of his eye. Upon reaching the ashram, he was startled to see it looking more beautiful than Amaravati, the abode of Indra.

At first, he didn't recognize the old rishi, who now was a handsome youth like the morning sun – radiant and calming. His beloved daughter was dressed in silk and maids were tending to her. The king's pain evaporated; he felt a surge of intense joy rushing through his entire being which was even greater than the happiness he had felt when his princess was born. It had been years since he had felt so strong and happy, and his depression simply disappeared. He fell at the sage's feet.

'I suddenly feel light, happy and at peace,' the king exclaimed. 'My illness has gone.'

'O King,' intoned the sage, 'you were not suffering from any illness in the first place: you were simply afflicted by your desires. Some desires you had to relinquish unwillingly when your daughter was married to me. Some you let go voluntarily when wisdom dawned on you the last time you came here, and the rest have been fulfilled by seeing your daughter happy today. Desires and desires alone were the cause of your feeling depressed.'

This is a Puranic legend.[14]

Many patients of depression are like the king of this legend: They are only suffering because life hasn't transpired the way they had envisaged. If that is the cause of your depression, popping antidepressants is clearly not going to help you. Besides, I don't believe that antidepressants can actually cure your depression, nor do I believe that there is some miraculous meditation which will allow you to transcend depression. Furthermore, superior food cannot restore your well-being in days; yoga postures will not eliminate depression and stress from your system in an instant, and there is no prayer that can summon all the powers of the universe for you.

But when you apply all of these – meditation, diet, yoga and prayer – over a period of time to cure your depression, you are plugging all the gaps; you are at once working on your physical, subtle and causal bodies. Indeed, because your approach is holistic, there is no power in the three worlds that can stop you from being healed.

What is this life if, full of care,
We have no time to stand and stare.
No time to stand beneath the boughs
And stare as long as sheep or cows.

No time to see, when woods we pass,
Where squirrels hide their nuts in grass.
 No time to see, in broad daylight,
Streams full of stars, like skies at night.

No time to turn at Beauty's glance,
And watch her feet, how they can dance.
No time to wait till her mouth can
Enrich that smile her eyes began.

A poor life this if, full of care,
We have no time to stand and stare.

– W. H. Davies[15]

9

The Sanctum Temple
Physical Healing

In his dramatic epic poem *Kumarasambhavam*, the great poet Kalidasa says *Shariramadyam khalu dharmasadhanam:* your body alone is the medium through which you do all good karma. There is no doubt that if we are not physically well, all flavours of the world appear tasteless. Unless we feel strong, energetic and healthy, we can't derive much pleasure from the joys of this world. Even a simple cup of coffee has no aroma and thus offers little delight if your nose is blocked, for example. Conversely, it is hard to imagine anyone being in peak physical form while in the throes of a serious mental illness.

The body and mind are inextricable; if the body is the hardware, the mind is the software. Unquestionably, your mental state has a powerful effect on your body and your physical health ineluctably influences your emotional and mental health. You can eat all the right foods and exercise well but if your mind is not supporting your body, such measures can do but little to improve your physical health.

This is one of the primary reasons, I have observed, why a majority of those endeavouring to lose weight are unsuccessful – even though they may stick to strict diets and rigorous exercise routines. What's in your mind matters as much here as what's in your stomach. Equally, a lifestyle which gives scant regard for physical health can barely be expected to support proper mental functioning and emotional well-being.

Of course, there is no single, prescriptive diet for optimal mental health, just as there is no exercise regime which is suitable for everyone's body. Ayurveda teaches that the same food can have a different impact on people based on their constitutions (prakriti). An Ayurvedic assessment of one's constitution is based on the three humours of wind (vata), bile (pitta) and phlegm (kapha). Further, Ayurveda states that beyond just being heavy or light on digestion, or being acidic (ushna or amla) or alkaline (sheeta or snigdha), foods can impart goodness (sattvic food), passion (rajasic food) or ignorance (tamasic food). At the risk of oversimplifying a very involved ancient teaching for the sake of understanding and correcting depression, it means that certain foods can make you feel calm and composed, some others can infuse you with passion, and some can provoke anger.

Ayurveda says that food is your foremost medicine. It considers the role of proper diet at par with – if not above – the consumption of medicine for healing. Food and medicine are intricately linked; even allopathic medicine acknowledges the importance of a salutary diet alongside medication in treating illness.

FOODS FOR NEUROTRANSMITTERS

Among the many sattvic (inherently healthy and good) foods that help to cure depression and other emotional disorders, most are alkaline. Before I list them, I would like to remind you that neurotransmitters are, by and large, chemical agents made from amino acids. Proteins are the source of amino acids, and to manufacture neurotransmitters they require vitamins and minerals.

Protein, vitamins (C and B), and minerals (calcium and magnesium) are needed to produce serotonin. Green leafy vegetables (especially spinach), brown rice, tofu, sunflower seeds and sesame seeds are full of the nutrients required for the production of serotonin. Walnuts, flaxseeds, hemp and chia seeds contain Omega-3 fatty acids that are excellent for raising serotonin levels. While eggs and fish are also good for serotonin production, yogic scriptures classify all meat and poultry as tamasic food. Tamasic foods are acidic, and their consumption provokes aggressive emotions.

Almonds, lentils, brown rice, beans, melons and cantaloupes are sattvic and alkaline foods that are excellent for neurotransmitter production, especially GABA. Oranges also assist in GABA production and regulation.

Ripe bananas are an excellent source of the compounds required to derive dopamine. Obversely, free radicals deplete dopamine levels; so if you eat food rich in antioxidants, you can help to protect your body's dopamine reserves. Most citrus fruits and berries are packed with antioxidants. Besides, the vitamins from these fruits combine with amino acids to produce neurotransmitters. Sesame seeds also help in dopamine production. Drinking coffee, alcohol and sugary drinks can deplete the body's dopamine levels. If you are not lactose-intolerant, you may consume milk and other dairy products to assist the production of neurotransmitters. Wheat germs are rich in nutrients that raise acetylcholine levels in the brain.

Eggs are also good for assisting acetylcholine production. Yogurt aids the production of neurotransmitters, but according to Ayurveda it has a negative impact on the cellular excretory system. Ayurveda states that each cell in the body has an inlet and an outlet and that yogurt blocks the outlet of the cells, creating a breeding ground for numerous ailments. Yogurt is also acidic in nature. But if you feel good after eating yogurt, feel free to eat it. In any case, it's not good to consume it after sunset (or before going to bed) as it vitiates the three humours of wind, bile and phlegm.

In summary, your dietary focus should be on consuming mostly alkaline foods.[16] Antidepressants often have devastating side effects, whereas your food – especially that which is alkaline – is mostly free of side effects. The type of food you eat has an immediate impact on your mental and physical state. For depression, certain foods stand out. One of them is mango. It boosts serotonin in your body. While you should generally avoid tea and coffee because they are highly acidic, in depression, coffee can actually be helpful – if it is enjoyed in moderation, of course. It lifts your mood. If you get used to eating mango, that can lift your mood just as well.

Folic acid found in spinach (boiled spinach) is very good too. A glass of orange juice has a positive impact. Besides the standard nutritional benefits, alkaline foods boost your neurotransmitters. Here's a food chart for your quick reference:

Neurotransmitter	Food
Serotonin	Mangoes, walnuts, flaxseeds, hemp and chia seeds, green leafy vegetables, tofu, sunflower seeds, brown rice, sesame seeds.
Dopamine	Sesame seeds, citrus fruits and berries, bananas.
GABA	Almonds, lentils, brown rice, beans, cantaloupes, oranges.
Acetylcholine	Poultry, wheat germs.

Although tea and coffee are stimulants and deplete neurotransmitters in the longer term, if taken in moderation, they can lift your mood. Yogurt also aids in production of neurotransmitters. Try to eat organic and alkaline foods as much as possible.

Let me remind you that neurotransmitters are made from amino acids that are found in the protein we consume through our diets. Protein alone can't manufacture neurotransmitters, though. In addition, you need the vitamins and minerals that are found in abundance in most alkaline and wholesome foods. If you eat wholesome foods and you eat organic food as much as possible, you can't go wrong. Ideally, no more than 20 per cent of your diet should consist of acidic foods.

Furthermore, most of your diet should consist of vegetarian foods items, because they are living foods. You might wonder what a living food is. Any food that can sprout has living energy in it. Eating living foods brings you one step closer to nature; and the closer you are to nature, the faster you will heal. Here are some golden pointers for you to combat depression:

- Try to eat vegetarian, organic and whole foods whenever you can.
- Avoid processed, canned, acidic and starchy foods.
- Eat strictly at the same time every day. This is most beneficial for the body. Above all, it keeps the metabolic processes in check including acid production in the body. It has a direct and instant effect on your health.
- Avoid long periods between your meals because, among other perils, this ultimately results in raised insulin levels. Eating wholesome foods at the same time every day and avoiding extended periods of time between your meals can also help you overcome binge eating and bulimia.
- Go to bed at about the same time every day. Even if you have insomnia or you can't go to sleep for any other reason, don't be stressed about it. Enjoy a shower, freshen up, and lie down in your bed. Don't worry about being unable to fall asleep. Just take deep breaths. It is best to sleep lying on your right side, as this will start the left nostril which is the lunar channel. Breathing through the left nostril has a cooling and calming effect on the body and mind.
- No matter what, don't replace your sleeping time with screen time. So if you can't go to bed, don't get up and watch TV or go online and surf the net. Trust me on this one (or validate it for yourself). You can listen to some light music; or better still, just listen to your breath. If you notice any disturbing thoughts creeping into your mind, pay no attention as a matter of principle – be resolute, and simply listen to your breath.
- Make sure that you eat approximately four hours prior to going to bed. This is absolutely critical for a sound, rejuvenating and nourishing sleep. If you find it hard to go to bed on an empty stomach, you can have a wholesome light snack (such as a piece of fruit or a piece or two of wholewheat bread with a slice

or two of cucumber – without cheese) an hour before you go to bed.

- The most important principle of maintaining a sound diet is: don't be obsessed. Listen to your body and eat in moderation.

If you have worked out physically during the day, and you have eaten the correct foods for your body type, regardless of your state of mind, you should sleep soundly.

THE YOGA POSTURES

There are numerous yoga postures that can work seeming miracles on your body and mind. Of hundreds of such postures, I have selected three that are particularly helpful in relieving depression. As a matter of strict practice, you should always lie down on your back for a few minutes and breathe gently to conclude your yoga session every day. Yoga can be done once, twice or three times a day depending on your time availability and your passion. A session can last anywhere from twenty minutes to an hour. An average session is of thirty minutes. Forty-five minutes is most common from start to finish; this is ample time to do all the postures with feeling and focus. Postures of yoga should not be mistaken as exercises for simply stretching the limbs. Every pore of your existence talks to you if you perform them with feeling, and that is how they yield the greatest result.

THE SUN SALUTATION

The sun salutation (Surya namaskara) is the mother of yogic exercises. It is not actually one posture, but a sequence of twelve yogic postures which should be performed with a focus on inhalation and exhalation. The Surya namaskara appears quite simple but is profoundly effective. It stretches your entire body and channels the flow of various energies. Here is how to do it:

The Sun Salutation

First Position

Take a deep breath. Stand straight, with your body relaxed. Bring your hands together and join them near your heart in the posture of namaste, and exhale.

Second Position

Start your inhalation and gently separate your hands. Raise your hands above your head, fully stretching your arms. Arch backwards with your palms facing towards the sky. Don't arch more than is comfortable.

Third Position

Exhale slowly and bend forward with your legs straight. Your head will rest between your knees, and ideally you should be touching the ground with your hands. If you can't bend so far as to touch the ground, bend as far as you can without straining.

Fourth Position

Bend your knees as if you are about to sit on the floor, and rest your palms flat on the floor. Stretch your left leg back with your toe touching the floor. Bring your right leg in front with your knee touching your chest and foot firmly planted flat on the ground. Raise your chin upwards and inhale gently and deeply.

Fifth Position

Stretch back your right leg. Raise your hips as if you are about to do a push-up. Keep your chin pressed against the upper part of your chest. Gently exhale while you move to the next posture.

Sixth Position

Stretch your legs back and lower yourself. Your palms, chest, knees and toes touch the ground. Your hips remain a little raised and your belly does not touch the ground at all. Your forehead is parallel to the ground but does not touch it. Hold your breath.

Seventh Position

Start inhaling gently. Straightening your arms, lower your legs and waist so that your toes, legs, knees, thighs and groin touch the floor, and raise your torso, gently arching back your spine. Raise your chin as if you are looking up and stretching your neck.

Eighth Position

Raise your hips and bring your straightened legs midway forward. Your body now forms a triangle. Lower your head and press your chin to your upper chest and exhale gently. Your palms and heels remain flat and firmly planted on the ground.

Ninth Position

Gently inhaling, stretch back your right leg, arching your spine, and bring forward your left leg so your knee touches your chest. The toe and knee of your right leg touches the ground and the left foot is flat on the ground. Your palms are flat on the ground. Raise your chin up. Now you are in the same posture as in the fourth position but with the alternate leg stretched.

Tenth Position

Bring your feet together, straighten your legs so you are upright and bend forward from the waist. Once again, try to touch the floor with your palms and if you can't, lower them as much as you can. Exhale gently.

Eleventh Position

Inhale deeply and gently. Straighten your body and arch backwards with your palms facing upwards. This is exactly the same posture now as in the second position.

Twelfth Position

Straighten your body, fully stretching the arms with palms facing each other and exhale gently, while bringing your hands together and joining them near your heart in the posture of namaste. This marks the conclusion of the sun salutation.

Hold each posture for a few seconds. This is one round. In the second round, alternate your legs – stretch the right leg first in the fourth position and the left one in the ninth. There is a variation of this posture where the same leg is stretched in the fourth and ninth position and is only alternated in the next round. Lying flat on your back for a few minutes in the corpse posture (shavasana) is highly recommended after completing your session of the sun salutation.

The ancient method of the Surya namaskara also involves chanting the seed syllables of the sun mantra while doing the sun salutation. Texts expounding the solar science believe that the rays of the first few minutes at sunrise are particularly therapeutic. Ideally, the sun salutation is performed facing the sun at the time of sunrise. If this is not feasible, you can do it indoors at the time you do yoga or other physical exercises. You can start by doing ten rounds every morning. With practice, your postures will effortlessly flow into each other in perfect transposition.

THE SHOULDER STAND

There are two postures that are not covered in the sun salutation. You will benefit much from doing these. The first one is called the shoulder stand. It is known as the sarvangasana in Sanskrit. Sarvanga means 'all organs' or 'part'. This posture imbues your entire body and mind with vitality. Your torso and legs are fully stretched as you raise yourself vertically with your neck bent and head on the

ground, while the weight of your entire body rests on your shoulders. You hold your body with your hands. Here are the steps to do it:

Lie on your back, relaxed but straight. Keep your legs together, with your ankles touching each other and your toes facing up. Keep your arms straight with your palms touching your thighs.

Gently inhale while you slowly raise your legs, so they are at an angle of 90° to your torso. Turn your palms downward to touch the floor. Exhale, and raise your body by pressing your hands hard against the floor while inhaling. Bring your hands onto your waist to support the torso as your hips rise off the floor. Raise the body as straight as possible. Keep your legs together all this time. The entire weight of your body should now rest on your shoulders (not on your neck or head), with your chin pressed against the upper part of your chest. Your toes should now be pointing at the ceiling. Breathe gently and normally. Remain in this position for thirty seconds. Gradually, you can increase the duration of the asana, but you should not, at any rate, perform it for longer than three minutes.

To complete the asana, gently bend your legs, folding

them at the knees and slowly lower your body to the floor, all the while using your hands to support your torso's weight. Once you are lying flat on the floor again, stretch your legs straight and breathe. This asana is prohibited for pregnant women and anyone who has undergone any form of heart surgery. Besides being good for depression, this posture is excellent for the spine, nervous system and thyroid glands. At the end of your yoga session, always lie down in the corpse pose for three to five minutes.

The shoulder stand is a variation of the head stand (shirshasana). The head stand is not recommended unless you are disciplined in your practice of pranayama (breath regulation) and completely free of any gastrointestinal, respiratory and neurological disorders.

THE CHILD POSE

This pose is called balasana. Bala means child. It is a simple and easy pose that nevertheless has a powerful calming effect on the body and mind. To perform the posture, follow the steps below:

Keep your feet apart at the width of your hips, and gently inhale as you kneel on your hands and knees, with your palms facing down. Straighten your toes so that your toenails touch the floor. Keep them relaxed, though. Exhale and lower your buttocks towards your heels, and assume an upright kneeling position with your hands placed palm downward on your thighs. This naturally stretches your torso. Bend forward with your arms extended in front of you until your forehead touches the floor and your arms are stretched along the floor in front of your head. Gently inhale and bring your arms back along the side of your thighs, with your palms facing up. Breathe slowly and hold this posture for thirty seconds. To complete the posture, bring your arms in front of your head again with your palms facing down, and return to the upright kneeling position with your hands palm downward on your thighs.

You can place a cushion between your buttocks and heels if the stretch is uncomfortable. Feel free to rest your forehead on a cushion if the floor feels hard or uncomfortable.

REGULATION OF BREATH

There is a term frequently found in most of the yogic scriptures. It's called pranayama. Prana means vital life force in the breath and yama means to elongate, strengthen or progress. Pranayama is the science of breath regulation. It is primarily of twelve different types. It has three stages called exhalation (rechaka), retention (kumbhaka) and inhalation (puraka). Pranayama is not for everyone; correct breath regulation requires attaining a perfect stillness in the posture and the observance of strict dietary guidelines and moral conduct. This is because through pranayama you infuse every pore of your body with the vital life force. If your state of mind is negative and the breath impure, this is what you will energize and supply to all your body's cells.

Each cell is a complete living unit in its own right. It has a respiratory system, an excretory system, a nervous system and an endocrine system. It even possesses a consciousness of sorts. The quality of life force you supply to each cell has a profound impact on the life and health of that cell. Pranayama is a powerful means of delivering vital energy, or prana, to each and every cell of your body. It is capable of opening clogged arteries; it makes the muscles supple, gives lustre to the skin, reduces stiffness in the joints and infuses life in the veins. Pranayama done wrongly, however, can lead to neurological disorders. That said, if you don't hold your breath during pranayama, you shouldn't have much to worry about. When you simply inhale and exhale in a specific way, it regulates your breath and immediately calms your mind. Of the many types of pranayama, I will share with you the two types that are particularly useful for overcoming depression.

Before you begin pranayama, it is important to sit with your back straight: your spine, neck and head must form a straight line. If you can sit cross-legged, it is even better, because this regulates the vital energies in the body. You can also sit in a chair. At least two hours should have elapsed between your last meal and the exercise of pranayama. If you do yoga and then pranayama, the rewards are multiplied and may be more quickly reaped. Let us get to the two types of pranayama for you.

ALTERNATE BREATHING

Alternate breathing is a type of pranayama that is excellent for neurological and respiratory cleansing and detoxification. It forms part of the purification of the nervous system (nadishodhana) regime. It is called anuloma–viloma in yogic texts. Anuloma means natural order and viloma means reverse order. Retention of breath (kumbhaka) is an important aspect of pranayama. Such breathing in its purest sense is recommended only for those who have mastered the physical posture, eat an exclusively sattvic diet and are complete teetotallers. As with many yogic practices, however, it may be practised in a gentler form by less advanced students, as part of their guided progression in the discipline. Therefore, if you are quite new to yoga or your lifestyle is less than 'yogic', my strong recommendation is that you do not hold your breath for any more than a few seconds (between five and ten at the most).

There is a very important reason to take this seriously. When you practise alternate breathing without mastering a stable posture and without controlling your diet, you run the risk of pushing toxins through your nervous system to all parts of your body. This can lead to neurological disorders, formation of tumours and cysts, and loss of memory. If you practise it without prolonged retention of breath, however, you gain the greatest benefit with little risk. You purify and cleanse your nervous system and boost the stabilizing energies in and around you. If you have been practising yoga for a long time (a minimum of two years) and you are on a sattvic diet, you can practise breath retention for a longer time. In any case, do not retain your breath beyond what is comfortable. No yogic exercise is supposed to make you red in the face – neither when you are doing it nor afterward. Yogic exercises are supposed to be effortless.

HOW TO DO IT RIGHT

Here are the seven steps to the life-transforming alternate-breathing pranayama:

1. Sit straight, preferably cross-legged, or you can sit on a chair.
2. As always, start with complete exhalation with both nostrils.
3. Put the thumb of your right hand on your right nostril to close it.
4. Now inhale deeply, steadily and gently through your left nostril.
5. Hold the breath for a few seconds.
6. Put the middle finger of your right hand on the left nostril and lift your thumb to open the right nostril.
7. Exhale completely, steadily and gently. Ideally, your exhalation should be so soft that you should not even hear yourself breathing.

Yogic scriptures state the standard one-four-two rule for pranayama. This means that if it takes you one second to breath in, for example, you should hold the breath for four seconds (four times the length of inhalation) and exhale over two seconds (double the length of inhalation). As I stated earlier, however, this should only be done if you have been guided by an expert and if you are observing all the rules.

If you have epilepsy or seizures, if you are on medication for hypertension or you suffer from palpitations of the heart, or if you have had a heart attack in the past, do not retain the breath at all. Simply just breathe from alternate nostrils. At one stretch you can do twenty repetitions. One complete repetition is: inhale from the left, hold, exhale from the right, inhale from the right, hold, and then exhale from the left. You are free to do it twice or even thrice a day, but very few people have the time for this. There is no better purifier of your entire nervous system than pranayama. It is nothing short of a miracle exercise handed down to us by the ancient yogis.

BUMBLEBEE BREATHING

This is called bhramari pranayama. Bhramara means bumblebee. As the name suggests, in this exercise you make the humming sound of a bumblebee. It has a nearly instant calming effect on the mind. Imagine a table with playing cards scattered on it. They are a mess. Furthermore, the cards on their own are flimsy; they are easily bent, torn or lost. Imagine now organizing those cards to form a neat deck, held together with an elastic band. With the cards thus consolidated, they have become strong, organized and unified. This affords them considerable strength. Similarly, when there is a mismatch between cellular organization and emotional and mental forces, the energies in your body are scattered and unaligned, and you are weak. Bumblebee breathing aligns those energies, and the effect is instant and palpable. With regular practice, you will notice your strength multiplying.

HOW TO DO IT RIGHT

Bumblebee breathing is an eight-step process as follows:

1. Sit straight, preferably cross-legged or you can sit on a chair.
2. Take a few deep breaths to become aware of your breathing and to normalize it.
3. Spread your hands and bring them to your ears.

4. Block your left ear with your left thumb and your right ear with your right thumb. Gently place your index and middle fingers of the right hand on your closed right eye.

5. Do the same on your left eye with your left index and middle fingers. Don't press your eyes.

6. Rest your ring fingers just below your eyes. Your mouth should be closed and your lips covered with your little fingers.

7. Now, inhale with both nostrils as deeply and comfortably as you can.

8. Gently exhale from both your nostrils, producing a humming sound like that of a bee.

Feel free to take breaks after a few rounds, as your arms and hands may get tired in that position after a few minutes. Resume the exercise after your break. You can do it up to twenty times in one session and you can do two sessions of bumblebee breathing a day. This pranayama has an extraordinary filtering effect on the body and mind.

All the yogic exercises I have detailed are indispensible for attaining a balanced mental and emotional state. To heal depression – and indeed, to enjoy a happy and fulfilling life – you should adhere to yogic practices and a healthy diet religiously. After all, your body is a sanctum, a temple – and as such, it should be revered and kept like one.

I know taking control of your health and changing your lifestyle is easier said than done. But if you focus on your diet, do the yoga postures and regulate your breathing, it'll have a profound impact on your physical, mental and emotional well-being. The stronger and more together you feel, the better prepared you are to work on healing yourself and attending to aspects of your life that need adjustment or radical change, as the case may be.

In any event, if you can replenish the depleted neurotransmitters in your body by adopting a healthier lifestyle, if you can receive a loving touch, if you can develop that rhythm in your breathing – you will never need to take another antidepressant. You don't have to take my word for this, or for any other suggestions I make in this book. Try it – and see it for yourself.

Gazing intently into the empty sky, vision ceases;
Likewise, when mind gazes into mind itself,
The train of discursive and conceptual thought ends
And supreme enlightenment is gained.

Like the morning mist that dissolves into thin air,
Going nowhere but ceasing to be,
Waves of conceptualization, all the mind's creation, dissolve,
When you behold your mind's true nature.

The darkness of a thousand aeons is powerless
To dim the crystal clarity of the sun's heart;
And likewise, aeons of samsara have no power
To veil the clear light of the mind's essence.

The mind's original nature is like space;
It pervades and embraces all things under the sun.
Be still and stay relaxed in genuine ease,
Be quiet and let sound reverberate as an echo,
Keep your mind silent and watch the ending of all worlds.

– Tilopa's song of Mahamudra

10

Thoughts Become Things
Mental Healing

A man in search of truth ended up at the monastery of a sage. Prostrating himself before the master, he requested refuge and expressed his desire to master his mind. The sage told him he was happy to initiate him, but there were certain rules the disciple would have to obey.

'I want you to practise silence,' the master said, 'Therefore, you are only allowed to speak once in every twelve years, only one sentence of no more than five words.'

The disciple readily agreed. For twelve years he tried to meditate and eagerly waited for his opportunity to speak.

'Bed is too hard,' he said to his guru at the first opportunity after twelve years.

'Hmm ...' the master grumbled.

The disciple was extremely upset to hear such an indifferent and short response from his master.

Another twelve years elapsed in silence and the disciple complained, 'Food is too cold.'

'Hmm ...' said the master.

The disciple felt even angrier, but he did not want to break the rule.

He meditated for another twelve years and then said, 'I'm leaving.' Exceeding the limit of five words, he continued, 'This is rubbish. I haven't gained anything, I haven't learned anything and you haven't taught me anything.'

'Good! Be gone,' the master replied, 'all I have heard you do in the last thirty-six years is complain, complain, and complain! If silence couldn't teach you what else can; from whom can you learn if you cannot learn from life?'

Many people, like the disciple in our story, are constantly complaining in their heads. I call it cerebral complaining, and it is a vicious trap. What's worse is that they are not even aware that it has become their habit. When you allow your mind to take control of you, it will ceaselessly toss you between positive and negative thoughts (sometimes between negative and more negative thoughts). The flow of thoughts is like the river of life, swelling and receding, then merging with the ocean of consciousness. There, among constant waves of thoughts, tides of emotions flood and ebb, and seemingly harmless swells rise in endless peaks and troughs over unseen currents. In these, the unwary are liable to founder.

A patient of depression is unable to swim from a whirlpool of depressing thoughts. As Rumi once said, 'O seeker, these thoughts have such power over you. From nothing you become sad, from nothing you become happy.' And this is the unvarnished truth. We are constantly affected by our thoughts, such that they become our reality. Our thoughts and fears manifest before us in the form of difficult situations, partners and bosses.

Most of us do battle with our thoughts. Someone gets

the thought of smoking and soon it turns into a craving. The more he resists it, the more powerful the craving for a cigarette becomes. It is simply not feasible to take control of your thoughts, because they are incessantly rushing through the mind. How can you stand against a raging torrent, a river in flood? It is possible to go to the source, however – that is, your mind – to either channel your thoughts or contain them. That being said, maintaining a tranquility of mind is an advanced stage of meditation. Until you attain this level of ability, Patanjali recommends in his aphorisms a powerful method of countering your negative and pessimistic thoughts:

> When improper thoughts disturb the mind, there should be constant pondering over the opposites. Improper thoughts and emotions such as those of violence – whether done, caused to be done, or even approved of – indeed, any thought originating in desire, anger or delusion, whether mild medium or intense – do all result in endless pain and misery. Overcome such distractions by pondering on the opposites.[17]

Thus, when life looks listless, just meditate on the opposite. Look around and see all you have to be grateful for. The nectar of gratitude easily washes away the poison of negativity. This is the act of conscious balancing.

Mahatma Gandhi prescribed a method to gauge the usefulness of one's actions and afford oneself a perspective beyond the bounds of self. This method, which he wrote in the months before his untimely death, cannot help but focus our thoughts on the blessings in our lives, and is thus a tonic against pessimist and negative thoughts.

> I will give you a talisman. Whenever you are in doubt, or when the self becomes too much with you, apply the

following test. Recall the face of the poorest and the weakest man whom you may have seen, and ask yourself, if the step you contemplate is going to be of any use to him. Will he gain anything by it? Will it restore him to a control over his own life and destiny? In other words, will it lead to swaraj [freedom] for the hungry and spiritually starving millions? Then you will find your doubts and yourself melt away.[18]

If you are holding this book, you are almost certainly in the more socio-economically privileged sector of the world's population. You would therefore have a roof overhead and adequate clothes to wear; you can afford medication and you don't go to bed hungry (unless by your own choice). If we give some consideration for the plight of the multitudes of hungry people – who account for as many as one in every nine people in the world – some of the material disappointments in our lives can simply melt away.[19] We can only feel grateful for our full bellies and comfortable beds after pondering the opposite. Moreover, this gratefulness can evoke a change of mental outlook, for one thought is always connected to another. If you develop the habit of holding on to positive thoughts, your mind will fill with positivity; imprints of negative thinking, which are the hallmark of depression, will be scratched out and overwritten with those conducive to a happy, productive state of being.

Besides making a habit of positive thought, the finest method of mental healing is meditation. It stills your body and your mind. Meditation, not sleep, is the true restful state. In this state, you become more mindful and aware of your thoughts, emotions and actions. Such awareness aligns the various energies in your body, puts you in greater control of yourself and makes you more at ease. In this chapter, I will share with you yogic practices to strengthen your concentration and a practical method of meditation. These will help you to attain a flawless and lucid meditative state. Let us begin with the yogic practice:

STILL GAZING

Stillness of the eyes controls many subtle energies in the body. Restless people tend to have 'shifty' eyes. Have you noticed chess players? They are so engrossed in their thinking while playing that you could mistake them for dead people. There is rarely any movement in their eyes. The same goes for artists, mathematicians and scientists. The more engaged your mind is in constructive thinking, the more still your gaze. The practice of still gazing is called trataka. It is the method of fixing your gaze on any chosen object. The ability to perfect your gaze is critical in attaining a true meditative state. Still gazing will make you feel calm and energized. Here's how to do trataka correctly:

1. Sit in a comfortable posture, preferably cross-legged.
2. Light a candle, at a distance of about three feet in front of you.
3. Ensure the candle or any other object of focus is at your eye level. Watching a flame is more energizing because a flame has dynamic energy.
4. Watch it for ten minutes. Ideally, you shouldn't blink while watching the candle. It is hard to not blink – at first, tears start rolling down your cheeks if you try to keep your eyes open without blinking – but with practice, your eyes will become used to the exercise. You should, however, do what is comfortable for you.

5. During the actual practice, try to be aware of your wandering thoughts, and gently bring your mind back to the object of focus.

Do trataka for ten minutes before going to bed, and you will have a peaceful sleep and a calmer mind when you waken. Trataka also helps in improving digestion because it has an impact on the ten vital energies – one of which is called the thermal energy (samana vayu) – directly responsible for producing digestive enzymes in the body. You can make this practice a part of your daily routine. You can start the meditation below once you have done still gazing for about forty days.

You'll be better prepared to meditate if you have learned the art of concentration first by practising still gazing.

WITNESS MEDITATION

At the root of feelings and emotions are thoughts, most of which live in the subconscious mind. From the subconscious springs a negative or a positive thought and sometimes the conscious mind grabs it. When you grab a thought and are unable to let it go, it can become a desire or an emotion.

Being aware of your thoughts, actions and emotions brings them to the forefront of your mind, from the ever active subconscious mind to the more controllable conscious mind. This awareness helps you check your negative thoughts and boost your positive ones. In witness meditation, you are simply a witness. You don't play the judge or the jury – you are not the plaintiff or the defendant; you are not the lawyer or the law – you are simply an observer. When you watch your thoughts without reacting to them, they lose the power to trouble you. They start to disappear.

To do witness meditation, follow the steps below:

1. Sit straight, preferably cross-legged but this meditation is just as effective even if you sit in a normal chair. Ideally, your spine, neck and head should be in a straight line.
2. Rest your hands in your lap if you are seated cross-legged or on your knees if you are sitting in a chair.
3. Just relax your arms and feel a sense of relaxation in your entire body.
4. Take a few deep breaths to normalize your breathing.
5. Gently close your eyes and wait for the thoughts to come and knock on the door of your consciousness.
6. Simply observe your thoughts.

Good thoughts, bad thoughts – right, wrong, moral, immoral, loving and hateful – they are all just thoughts. Intrinsically, they are immaterial. Don't give them any importance – don't pursue them, don't react to them; and most importantly, don't talk to them. Just let them be. They will emerge, manifest and disappear. Let them. One by one they will come unceasingly; simply let them come.

When you no longer react to your thoughts with this meditation, a strange thing starts to happen: the gap between one thought and the next increases. This gap is a sort of quietude, a type of mental stillness. It's like you are going on a long drive. You are concentrating on the road and traffic and as you move out of the city, you hit the highway; you become a bit more relaxed. After a while, you notice a signpost pointing towards a scenic lookout point. You make a stop there – you are away from the rushing cars on the highway, you are away from all noise. You step out of your car and you take a deep breath. The air is clean and fragrant. You behold from your vantage point the grandeur of mountains stretching to the horizon, giving way to a fertile valley below. A quiet phase in meditation is like being at that vantage point.

Witness meditation helps you become more mindful. When you don't react and become a silent observer, nature takes control of your life, and your personal struggle disappears. And nature is replete with extraordinary, if not miraculous, healing forces. When you no longer put the onus on yourself but leave it to nature to fix whatever has gone wrong in your system, it won't disappoint you. You just have to stay true to your practice and your life.

The power of a quiet and focused mind is infinitely more than the restless and scattered one. You can do witness meditation for ten minutes in the morning and ten minutes before going to bed. With regular practice, you will come to know a quiet and focused mind.

I have some other pointers that may well be of use to you. These can elevate your mood and mental state. Listening to good music not only makes you feel good but it actually raises the level of neurotransmitters in the brain. So, feel free to listen to devotional songs or pleasant music to your taste. This will also help you take your mind off any worldly thoughts – especially negative ones.

Try to maintain a happy disposition. Even an artificial smile loosens up many stressed nerves. And what about a real smile? Well, there's no real difference – in this respect, at least. So smile anyway you like. There are many other, better and more attractive activities too that loosen up stressed nerves; but I had better leave those to your imagination. If you are religious, you may benefit by going to your place of worship or by participating in social programmes. When you go to sleep, make sure you start by sleeping on your right side. This activates the lunar channel, left breath, and brings down your body temperature. Discriminating faculties of the restless mind calm down significantly when breathing through the left nostril. Even a tiny drop in body temperature has a marked positive effect on mental quiescence.

If you believe in God, it will surely give you comfort to know that you are an instrument in the hands of the Divine and that He is looking after you. One who seeks His sanctuary, basks in His Grace unconditionally.

You are what your deep, driving desire is.
As your desire is, so is your will.
As your will is, so is your deed.
As your deed is, so is your destiny ...

So it is said:

When all the desires that surge in the heart
Are renounced, the mortal becomes immortal.
When all the knots that strangle the heart
Are loosened, the mortal becomes immortal.

– The Brihadaranyaka Upanishad[20]

11

Wipe Your Slate Clean
Emotional Healing

Let us examine emotional healing, beginning with the most difficult of emotions. I'm not talking about anger, jealousy, envy, sadness or even hatred. With great mindfulness, you can transcend these and other feelings. Above and beyond ordinary states of being is an emotion, a divine boon that is the essence of eternal peace.

Buddha once decided to leave his abode and travel for a time. He asked his chief disciples, Ananda, Shariputra and others, to stay back at the monastery as he ventured out on his own. This was most unusual because generally wherever Buddha went, he was invariably accompanied by his devotees and disciples; and they doted on him and revered him more than their own lives. They always wanted to be in his presence to behold his beautiful form, to listen to his tranquil words – and above all, just to serve him. But this time, Buddha had instructed them not to follow him until he said otherwise.

As he walked from one village to another, Buddha was

free to explore new places, for most people did not recognize him. They didn't think he was Gautama Buddha because there was no entourage, there was no crowd in his wake. He wandered discreetly like any other monk, humble and alone. One day on his travels, Buddha approached a man for alms. The man, though, was distraught and livid – his only cow had died just a short while earlier. In a fit of rage, he began shouting at Buddha and hurled foul abuse at him. The sage kept quiet and walked away. But a villager close by felt Buddha's unmistakable presence and recognized him.

He pacified the angry man and said, 'Do you know who he is?'

'What do I care?' the man replied.

'You should care. He is none other than Tathagata, the Buddha himself.'

'What are you saying?' the man exclaimed. 'It's not possible. Buddha always has a large crowd following him. Where are his disciples?'

'That I don't know, but I can tell you that he was Buddha. I've heard he's travelling on his own.'

The man was guilt-ridden and decided to find the sage so that he could beg his pardon. The next day, he traced Buddha and fell at his feet.

'Forgive me, O Sage!' he said. 'I'm truly ashamed for calling you names. Please punish me so that I may be purified.'

'Punish you for what?' Buddha asked calmly.

'For swearing at you, my lord.'

'When did you do that?'

'Yesterday,' he said.

'I don't know yesterday,' Buddha said. 'I know only today.'

This great emotion, this most healing of all processes, is forgiveness. Forgiveness is the hardest of all human emotions. It is also easily the most divine. There is, nevertheless, a difference between granting someone pardon and actually experiencing forgiveness as an emotion. Let me explain the subtle difference. When someone admits his wrongdoing and apologizes to you, and you pardon him, this is an act of forgiveness. This is nothing momentous, though, because he has admitted his mistake. If he is honest and committed to not repeat it, his sincerity will melt you. A more profound forgiveness, however, is that which relies on neither the confession nor contrition of the transgressor. This is yet a higher state of the same emotion; near the pinnacle of spiritual attainment, it is next only to the deepest of compassion. The ability to experience (and not merely exercise) such forgiveness is truly the most liberating of all human emotions.

Often, people hold on to grudges like some prized possessions. They don't want to let go, even when they can. But as it is, life is hard enough. Why they make it harder by eternally stocking more and more hard feelings is as much intriguing as it is a confounding aspect of human behaviour. Let us not forget that today could be our last. Every day is a new beginning. We brush, we bathe, we dress, we eat to start our new day. Why not actually make it new? Why not remind yourself every morning, 'Today, I'll not allow my past to barge into my present. Today, I'll meet all people as if I'm meeting them for the first time.' 'Is it even possible?' you may ask. Well, yes. If you can learn the art of erasing your psychic imprints, you can live your life as if each dawn brings you truly a new day – a day free of the baggage of yesterday and worries of tomorrow.

Psychic imprints, and in this sense emotions, are stored in the form of images, words and, at times, physical sensations.

For instance, in the case of one who has endured physical abuse, the physical wounds may well heal completely over time. But the mind's uncanny ability to store and recall thoughts in the form of images and words, and even to physically feel sensations of pain as psychic imprints, will perhaps cause greater and more lasting damage. In your quiet moments, when you recall painful incidents, you naturally feel indisposed. The more you try to forget them, the heavier they become; the faster you try to run away from them, the quicker they overtake you. In such moments, even the most promising methods for healing rarely work.

Emotional healing is of two types: natural and conscious. Natural healing can take a long time, such that it sometimes never completes. The practice of conscious emotional healing – of erasing the psychic imprints of images, words and sensations – is a deliberate effort. And the greater your effort in this, the better and quicker is your healing.

Feeling depressed, angry, constrained, down, pensive and so forth are most often the symptoms of emotional wounds. These mean you are still hurt somewhere within; the pain is still there. You may have simply suppressed it – but suppressing your pain only means it will, sooner or later, burst forth with a vengeance. Rather than fighting the symptoms, you need to go to the source of the pain to heal yourself. I will now share with you two of the finest methods of emotional healing.

THE YOGIC METHOD

The yogic method is the more difficult of the two, but it is foolproof. It is a form of meditation. If you meditate in your daily life or if you have patiently gone through the practice of meditation outlined in Chapter 10, 'Thoughts Become Things: Mental Healing', you will have no problem in practising this method. The resultant healing from this not only helps you come out of depression but restores your physical and mental health; you will feel even better than before.

The success in all yogic practices depends on your ability to sit still, to concentrate and visualize. Maintaining one posture stills the primary energies, concentration stills the five secondary energies[21] and readies your mind; and visualization is the actual healing exercise. The longer you are able to hold on to your visualization during your session of meditation, the quicker the healing. Visualization is like performing surgery: the patient (mind) needs to be perfectly still (with a proper posture and mental focus) while the surgeon (you) concentrates and does the procedure (visualization).

The yogic method is particularly useful when a certain event, like loss of a loved one, failure in its many guises, a relationship break-up or rejection, etc., has triggered your depression. Also, if you endured painful relationships or incidents in your childhood or adolescence, you may use this method to erase their imprints.

Here are the steps:

1. Posture: Sit still with your back straight, preferably crossed-legged, but any other comfortable posture will do just fine for this practice.
2. Close your eyes.
3. Breathe: Do deep breathing, just normal deep breathing, for a few minutes. The discriminating faculties of the conscious mind will become somewhat passive as a result.

4. Recall a person or an incident that caused you great grief in the past. Your mind will automatically pick up all related emotions and thoughts. Try to stay on that one person or incident.

5. Visualization: Imagine releasing soft white light from your heart chakra in the form of compassion and forgiveness. Anahata chakra, known as the heart chakra, is a psychoneural plexus situated near your heart, in the centre of your chest (the vertical middle point between your throat and navel, between the two nipples). If you experience guilt because you did something wrong, visualize forgiving yourself. If you feel you are at fault for what you had to go through, forgive yourself still. You will unearth a whole gamut of emotions as you do this practice. Bring your attention and focus to the calming white light. Visualize yourself being infused with it. Do not hesitate from engaging in self-dialogue; your intent, however, should not be to binge and brood over matters but to erase the imprint. It is not about right or wrong; it is just about forgiving for your own good. Clean the whole canvas of images. Repaint it with your favourite scene. Imagine yourself blissful and smiling; envision living your dream: being happy, being healthy.

6. Take a few deep breaths again and slowly open your eyes.

7. If you believe in God, say your favourite prayer, or simply express your gratitude for all that you have been blessed with.

One session should last at least fifteen minutes. Be consistent. Do not expect results in the first session. In fact, the first few times, you may even feel more down because you have just lifted the scab of an old wound. But remember that there is infection underneath: you need to do this so you may cleanse the wound for permanent healing. After a few sessions, you will feel elevated.

While you will start to see results after doing it only about ten times, real benefits will come if you persist. After you perform this practice a certain number of times – perhaps around thirty times – you will experience a miracle: you will find that recalling that incident or person no longer aggravates or irritates you. On the contrary, you will experience peace upon such recollections. You have now successfully transformed, metamorphosed your emotion. It is a beautiful feeling – and it is empowering.

Most yogic methods require an average of twenty-eight days of daily practice before they show any results. You thus need to set aside fifteen minutes daily for the next twenty-eight days to practise this method. It usually takes six months before an aspirant starts to perfect any yogic practice. Once you are able to practise intense visualization, you can accomplish just about anything you can imagine. Subsequent healing sessions accomplish much more, a good deal more quickly.

Once you see the results from this method, you will feel automatically motivated to go beyond. However, if you find it hard to meditate or visualize, you can opt for the intellectual method.

THE INTELLECTUAL METHOD

This is a relatively easy method and is based primarily on psychology. Think about what happens when a child gets a new toy. She is fascinated. The more she gets to play with it, the quicker her attraction starts to wither away. She gets over the toy. Earlier she would even sleep with it, talk to it, play with it; now, the toy is dead. Its sighting does not trigger any emotion in the child. Similarly – and just as naturally (albeit ironically) – when you experience abuse, rejection, failure, deceit, lies and pain, your mind gets a new toy. The more you try to avoid it, the stronger the attraction. Here is an easy way to get over those emotions. To carry out this practice effectively, you either need a mirror or a voice recorder. The steps are:

1. Look in the mirror or turn on the voice recorder.
2. Recall a negative or painful incident from your past.
3. Narrate it verbally, either by talking to the mirror or recording in your dictaphone.
4. Try to recall every minute detail around the incident. For example, let us assume someone you deeply loved broke up with you. The news itself was most unexpected. And the timing and manner of the break-up and the demeanour of your loved one – combined with your lack of anticipation of the event – made this a most traumatic experience. Years have passed, but you have not got over it. As part of this exercise, recall the incident. Do this boldly. Think of the colour of the walls, what you ate prior to being given the news, what all of you were wearing, what was going through your mind, how the other person looked, what objects were there in the room and what were the surroundings. Recall all these and speak them out aloud.
5. Take a few deep breaths and close the session.

You will experience pain and hurt. You may experience an emotional outpouring. Be bold. Do all this multiple times over a number of sessions. Play with this toy. You can later listen to your own recording. As you do, you will recall even greater detail. Over a period of time, as you do your sessions, the whole incident – the person and that phase of your life – will cease to matter. You may even find holding on to that particular pain or incident amusing after a few sessions. After fifteen to twenty sessions, its impact will simply disappear. Forever.

It is paramount to recall as much detail as possible. And here is why. Remember Bo? If you do not recall the detail, you will not be able to erase the pain. If you are unable to erase it, whenever you see similar coloured walls, people with similar expressions – even similar food that you had that day – it will silently trigger the negative or draining emotion in you. You will feel depressed, seemingly without cause. The truth is that the imprint has triggered your feeling. You or those around you may not understand what suddenly went wrong; but now you know. This is the primary reason why our moods fluctuate several times throughout the day. Various images, words and things trigger our reactions in the subconscious.

Hence, I cannot stress enough the importance of recalling as much detail as possible when you perform this exercise. The information recall in the fifth session, for instance, will be much greater than in the first. So repeat this exercise till you get over the incident completely. The devil is in the detail.

You may also do this exercise with a friend who is willing to listen to you without judgement. You could take turns. You could help the other person heal, and they could help heal you. That is why sharing – talking it out with someone who is not judgemental – can make you feel lighter. Each time you talk it out, it further reduces the hurt of the painful emotions associated with the traumatic event. This is the reason why people tend to share their ordeals with their friends. It is the mind's natural coping mechanism. When you speak about matters of concern or pain, their imprint softens.

No imprint means no pain. No pain means you are healed. Healing of the mind is almost like returning to your original state of peace and bliss; of joy and happiness; of compassion and tolerance. It's like being born into a new skin – or perhaps it's more like slipping the new you into the same skin (body).

Other than working on erasing the imprints of negative experiences to heal yourself, you should pursue that which makes you happy and brings you joy. In the ideal world, you would have the full support of your friends and family, who steadfastly encourage you to do whatever gives you a sense of fulfilment. Nothing heals faster than love and care. The security that a sense of belonging engenders can do miracles. If you don't have such supportive people around you, it will help your cause if you take charge of your life and work on your own healing. Some of the following options may appeal to you.

Do some selfless service or engage in an emotionally fulfilling social or spiritual cause. If you like the outdoors, painting, cooking, reading, dancing or any other salutary, life-affirming activity, do it. Distance yourself from those who drain you emotionally. This is a time when it is you who need a strong shoulder to lean on and a good listener. A warm conversation can be truly healing. In any case, try not to talk about your depression to those who either don't understand it or have little empathy. Most people will say there is nothing to worry about and that you are just stressed, and others cannot do a thing to help you, anyway.

Everyone else is likely to suggest that you visit a therapist. All this is nothing that you didn't already know.

Depression is not a type of fear that you need to face like a warrior and decimate. It is a state of mind, albeit an undesirable, dysfunctional one. The more you understand it, the better you can handle it. The more you take care of yourself, the quicker you'll come out of it. Treat yourself with care, with love, with compassion. Depression can bring a feeling of great inadequacy, but you and I both know that this feeling is illusory. The self-help author Marianne Williamson brilliantly sums up our predicament, exhorting us to see the true light within and let it shine:

> Our deepest fear is not that we are inadequate. Our deepest fear is that we are powerful beyond measure. It is our light, not our darkness that most frightens us. We ask ourselves, Who am I to be brilliant, gorgeous, talented, and fabulous? Actually, who are you not to be? You are a child of God. Your playing small does not serve the world. There is nothing enlightened about shrinking so that other people will not feel insecure around you. We are all meant to shine, as children do. We were born to make manifest the glory of God that is within us. It is not just in some of us; it is in everyone and as we let our own light shine, we unconsciously give others permission to do the same. As we are liberated from our own fear, our presence automatically liberates others.[22]

If you ponder nature, you will understand that the universe moves freely. Soaring mountains give way to deep valleys and water to mighty rivers; rivers meander seaward and pour into boundless oceans; oceans proffer clouds, returning water as minuscule drops to the very same mountains. There's no yesterday, just a constant flow.

In the same profound depths of your being and highs of your ecstasy, you'll realize that you are likewise complete and free; and a sense of freedom is the most healing balm of nature. Whatever it is that you are holding on to, it's restricting your freedom – it's limiting you. Freedom is strength, it is love. Let go.

Sheikhs, pirs and preachers cry,
At the moment of death, they all have to go.
Even the kings cry and dressed like fakirs,
They go around seeking alms.

The miser cries
for having to leave his wealth behind,
The scholar cries
for he can't carry his learning into his next life,

The young woman cries
for she has no one who loves her,
O Nanak, the whole world is suffering.

– Guru Nanak[23]

12

Seeing Wood For The Trees
What Isn't Depression

I was sitting, eagerly waiting for my order to be served at this amazing Italian restaurant in the Blue Mountains near Sydney. The sun had long gone below the horizon, the mercury had dipped and it was chilly outside. But inside it was warm and cosy, just how you feel when you are secure and happy in your heart. I casually looked to my left, and there was this beautiful quote framed on the wall. It was a long quote, but so insightful that it became etched in my mind:

> For years I thought, real life was about to begin. For years I thought something big, something grand was going to happen in my life and I would suddenly start feeling happier. I thought what I was living was not my real life, that I was meant to do something else. And one day I would be free of all shackles, I would be free of all my engagements. Then I would embark upon this journey of discovering myself, of being happy, of always being fulfilled. But there was always some unfinished business.

There was a bill to be paid, there was a call to be made, and there was an email to be replied to ... so, no matter how much I ticked off, there was always some stuff still left. There was always some obstacle on the path of my happiness.

One day, it dawned that these obstacles were my life.

We do everything we can to avoid suffering because we want peace, happiness and a life free of stresses and strains. We desire a life that's smooth and has no surprises and shocks for us. We want the future to announce itself before it arrives on the doorstep of our present. We want nature to go according to our plans. The truth is, we want too many things. We have unreasonable expectations from life. Not all sadness is depression, and peace is not about being free from stressful work. It is about seeing purpose and finding joy in what we have to do.

A king once wondered if peace could be depicted, and if so, what it would look like. He announced a grand prize for the artist who could paint the most apt picture of peace. Numerous artists from his empire crafted beautiful paintings. Some depicted birds and the vast sky. Others painted a calm ocean, while many the dense forests. One artist had drawn a mother feeding her child and another an old man sitting under a tree. Scores of other maestros brought life to their canvases with glorious colours and virtuosic skill. After much deliberation, the king shortlisted two paintings he felt were the closest representation of peace.

One painting was of a calm lake. Perfectly still, it was surrounded by colossal, lushly forested mountains. The benign expanse overhead was interrupted only by fluffy white clouds. An old tree stood by the lake with its boughs extending several feet over the water, upon which a dry leaf floated like a child's toy. The king's courtiers and his subjects proclaimed this the perfect representation of peace.

The other painting was of chaos writ large across the canvas. Whereas this too portrayed mountains, they were rugged and bare. The sky was of gunmetal grey rent by silver streaks of lightning, and driving rains lashed the landscape. A mighty waterfall gushed from a crevasse between the tall peaks. Everyone was puzzled to see this as one of the shortlisted paintings. But the king asked them to look closely, to examine the work more deeply. Beside the waterfall, a young bush grew in a fissure in the rock. There sitting amongst its leaves, in the centre of this tumult, was a nest where a mother bird was feeding her little ones – unafraid, and in perfect peace.

The king awarded the prize to this painting, 'Because,' said the king, 'the first painting is attractive, but it's not real. Peace doesn't mean a life devoid of adversities, troubles and challenges. Instead, it means to be surrounded by all of these and yet maintain faith and calm. That is the real meaning of peace.'

Most of us want the painting of our lives to look like the first one, but most often life hands us the second one. The first painting is our expectation from life and the second is the reality of it. And peace lies in reconciliation of the two. You can't stop the rains or the foaming waterfalls, but you can find your nest of life on the bush of faith – of acceptance, of good karma. This is no small feat, however, because we seem to be wrestling with the negative side of human nature much of the time.

A recent study in Belgium found that compared to twenty-seven other positive and negative human emotions, sadness lasts 240 times longer.[24] Just as a sponge only needs to touch water for a moment to become saturated, we seem to have a tendency to be affected by the smallest of untoward incidents. You ask someone to pass the salt at the dinner table and if he ignores you, you feel bad. Even this tiny incident can trigger emotions of sadness, and suddenly you may stop enjoying your meal or not feel like eating altogether. This is the way of sadness.

Perhaps nature could have primed us a bit differently. It would be nice if God hadn't rushed to create the world in six days. He could have taken it a bit easy – maybe he could have consulted. It's always good to do a pilot project first, I feel. What's worse is that after creation, he went to rest on the seventh day and seems to have left us to our own devices since. He still appears to be resting, while humans are left here to grapple with their existence, writing and reading books about depression.

Anyway, getting back to the reality of our world, the researchers in this revealing Belgian study wrote, 'Out of twenty-seven emotions, sadness lasted the longest, whereas shame, surprise, fear, disgust, boredom, being touched, irritation and relief were the shortest emotions. In particular, compared to short emotions, persistent emotions are typically elicited by events of high importance, and are associated with high levels of rumination.'

Sadness has this way of turning us into ruminators. When we are sad, we keep rethinking the same unpleasant event, over and over again. As is mind's wont, it soon dredges up all other related or unrelated disagreeable events. They start adding up and before long, we are caught in the whirlpool of intense sadness. This does not mean we are depressed, though.

When you say you are depressed, it may not be the same as when psychiatrists say you are depressed. It is important to understand their view because when a psychiatrist diagnoses you with depression, he almost invariably prescribes you antidepressants.

The *Diagnostic and Statistical Manual of Mental Disorders* (or *DSM* as it's commonly known) is the American Psychiatric Association's official guide of recognized mental disorders, and it contains the criteria for diagnosis for each disorder. The guide has been translated into more than twenty-two languages and is used by health care professionals worldwide. When they diagnose anyone with any mental disorder, this is the guide they refer to. According to *DSM*-V (the fifth edition launched in 2013), there are nine factors that define depression.

For anyone to be diagnosed with depression, they must experience at least five of the nine symptoms almost every day for a minimum of two weeks. If your symptoms match this clinical criteria (minimum five symptoms, two weeks, almost every day), you are diagnosed with depression and you are prescribed antidepressants almost as a matter of course.

See the table below for the nine factors and their description that make up the criteria for major depressive episode:

Criteria	Description
Depressed mood	You feel sad and empty, or even irritable or tearful, for most of the day. It could be based on self-observation or observation done by others.

Criteria	Description
Diminished interest	Marked diminished interest or loss of pleasure in almost all activities. Once again this could be based on subjective account (self-observation) or as reported by others.
Body weight	Significant weight loss or weight gain, that is, more than 5 per cent in one month even when you are not dieting. In young adults, if they don't gain new weight, consider it as weight loss.
Sleep pattern	A distorted sleep pattern leading to hypersomnia or insomnia.
Body movements	Psychomotor agitation or retardation. Psychomotor agitation is a series of unintentional and purposeless motions that stem from mental tension and anxiety of an individual. This includes pacing around a room, wringing one's hands, uncontrolled tongue movement, pulling off clothing and putting it back on and other similar actions.[25] Psychomotor retardation involves a slowing down of thought and a reduction of physical movements in an individual.[26]
Energy level	A constant feeling of fatigue or loss of energy.
Self-view	Low self-esteem, most notably, feelings of worthlessness and excessive or inappropriate self-guilt. These feelings are often delusional and not just feeling guilty about being unwell or not mixing with others.

Criteria	Description
Concentration	Diminished ability to think or concentrate. It could also be indecisiveness. This is not just due to restlessness or torpor, it is lack or loss of focus on its own.
Destructive thoughts	Recurrent thoughts of death (not just fear of dying), recurrent suicidal ideation without a specific plan, or a suicide attempt or a specific plan for committing suicide.[27]

Here are some important pointers:

1. One of the symptoms must be either 'Depressed mood' or 'Diminished interest'.
2. The symptoms do not meet criteria for a mixed episode.
3. The symptoms cause clinically significant distress or impairment in social, occupational or other important areas of functioning.
4. The symptoms are not due to the direct physiological effects of a substance (e.g., a drug of abuse, a medication) or a general medical condition (e.g., hypothyroidism).
5. The symptoms are not better accounted for by bereavement, i.e., after the loss of a loved one, the symptoms persist for longer than two months or are characterized by marked functional impairment, morbid preoccupation with worthlessness, suicidal ideation, psychotic symptoms, or psychomotor retardation.[28]
6. The episode is not attributed to the physiological effects of a substance or any other medical condition.

7. The occurrence of the major depressive episode is not better explained by schizo-affective disorder, schizophrenia, schizophreniform disorder, delusional disorder, or other specified and unspecified spectrum and other psychotic disorders.
8. There has never been a maniac or a hypomaniac episode.[29]

If you have experienced most of the symptoms stated in the table for a continuous period of more than two weeks, you are suffering from depression and you should seek professional help. Never feel bad about taking antidepressants. It's a medication and not a recreational drug. As I said earlier though, antidepressants are a means to an end. As part of your recovery, you should factor in dietary and lifestyle changes so that you may come off medication at the earliest.

If, however, you are sad or intensely sad because you find yourself ruminating about the past, or you were in an abusive relationship or anything else that has made you feel helpless and sad, you may want to reconsider if you are actually even suffering from depression. Living in a suffocating environment can make everything in life appear lacklustre; it can make you depressed, but it is not the type of depression that is likely to be cured by antidepressants.

When you continue to live in a distressing environment, you develop a normal behaviour of sadness. Aristotle differentiated between a melancholic temperament and a melancholic episode. The former becomes part of one's personality and the latter is a one-off happening.

The American psychotherapist and author Eric Maisel expresses a most interesting view of sadness, which he refers to as 'unhappiness':

> Let us be mature and truthful and accept the reality of unhappiness. It is not the coloration of life, but it is certainly one of life's colors. Moments of unhappiness happen. Days of unhappiness happen. Unhappiness can cloud a year or a decade. This does not make you 'disordered,' and it is nothing you should feel embarrassed about.[30]

I know what Dr Maisel is saying – and it makes sense too; but at the same time, depression is a very real condition. I've written this book with a belief that we must use our wisdom to distinguish depression from sadness. And whether you have 'depression' is a conclusion only you can draw, for you alone know your innermost thoughts and emotions.

If depression is comparable to a physical disease, it's certainly not just a common cold – it's more like a tumour. It could be benign in some or downright cancerous in others. Either way, it needs attention, because it is debilitating. Unlike many physical afflictions, though, it is curable; we can emerge from depression and lead happy, healthy lives. And that's just about the only kind side of depression.

Thou hast made me endless,
such is thy pleasure.

This frail vessel thou emptiest again and again,
and fillest it ever with fresh life.

This little flute of a reed thou hast carried
over hills and dales,
and hast breathed through
it melodies eternally new.

At the immortal touch of thy hands
my little heart loses its limits in joy
and gives birth to utterance ineffable.

Thy infinite gifts come to me
only on these very small hands of mine.
Ages pass,
and still thou pourest,
and still there is room to fill.

– Rabindranath Tagore[31]

13

Till the Cows Come Home

Let us forget for a moment the mechanics of medicine, the details of diagnosis, the workings of mind, the reality of suffering – all this tedious stuff and everything else we think we ought to know about depression.

As William Cowper wrote once, 'Your sea of troubles you have passed, and found the peaceful shore; I, tempest-tossed and wrecked at last, come home to port no more.' This is how suffering feels in depression: that it will never end, or that your world has ended. But you know that this is simply not true. You have had countless beautiful moments also – and you will continue to have beautiful moments if you persevere with wisdom.

Maybe you have had the pleasure of watching stars at night or walking on the beach in the mornings. Perhaps you have a roof over your head and you have clothes in your cupboard. You may have had the privilege of loving someone and being loved in return. Probably, your parents took you to the park when you were growing up or on a vacation. Do you remember your first kiss or the first touch? If you were to recall all that has been bestowed upon you, you will quickly realize how fortunate and blessed you are compared to hundreds of millions of people out there.

When you are sad or down, when everything is topsy-turvy, at that moment, just sit down and take a deep breath. Think about all you have to be grateful for. Write this down if you are not disposed to thinking clearly. We live in a world where hundreds of millions of people go to bed hungry (not by choice), where millions shiver every night in the cold, where millions die because they can't afford to buy medication. You and I live in the same world.

Maybe you are seated in an air-conditioned or a heated room while reading this book, or you have just left some food on your plate because you are full. Perhaps you have just bought a coffee. Let me tell you, this is more than we deserve. I know you realize that there are an astonishing number of our fellow brothers and sisters who will never have this luxury. If this is not enough to be grateful, what is? Gratitude is the antidote to intense sadness. You can either be grateful or you can be sad. Take your pick.

When you feel disconnected with the whole world, as if you don't belong to anyone and no one belongs to you, again, just sit down and take a deep breath. And think about all whom you could serve. Or once again, write this down if you are not disposed to thinking clearly. Perhaps there's an old-age home where you could go and serve coffee or cookies. Or an orphanage where you could get children doughnuts or chocolates. You could work with a charitable organization or raise funds for a cause you hold dear to your heart.

Maybe you could try and look beyond your own existence, because let me tell you, when you take up a cause bigger than yourself, the whole universe summons itself to be by your feet, waiting for your order. Immense strength and capacity flow to you as naturally as rivers flow to the ocean, and you attract resources just as effortlessly. To serve others is the surest way to rise above individual suffering, and serving humanity is assuredly the greatest means of belonging to this world.

In *The Dark Night of the Soul*,[32] there's a deeply moving passage. I quote:

> An old priest, abandoned by his community, sick and dying and terribly depressed, lifted his eyes and whispered, 'Oh, Jesus, I do love you so.' He smiled at me, his face was filled with hope, and his smile filled me with hope. And in the summer of 1994 I joined a small pilgrimage to Bosnia. I had the opportunity to speak with poor people who had lost everything: homes, possessions, entire families. As they told us their stories through tears of grief, I sensed deep hope in them. Through interpreters I asked if it were true.
>
> 'Yes, hope,' they smiled.
>
> I asked if it was hope for peace.
>
> 'No, things have gone too far for that.'
>
> I asked if they hoped the United Nations or the United States would intervene in some positive way.
>
> 'No, it's too late for that.'
>
> I asked them, 'Then, what is it you are hoping for?'
>
> They were silent. They could not think of a thing to hope for, yet there it was – undeniable hope shining in them.
>
> I asked one last question. 'How can you hope, when there's nothing to hope for?'
>
> The answer was, 'Bog,' the Serbo-Croatian word for God.

When you drive at night, you may only see twenty metres in front of you, but as you keep driving, the road continues to appear; and you can cover thousands of miles this way. Let the beauty of life unfold thus, one moment after another, and you will not be disappointed. No matter how dire the circumstances, we cannot afford to let go of hope. Perhaps, if there's only one thing worth holding on to, it is hope. When all seems dark and foreboding, sit down and take a deep breath. Just reflect on the forces of nature that are sustaining a myriad of other life forms – creatures of the water, earth and sky – trees, plants, flowers; everything is finding its food. Selfless forces – call it God, Nature, the Divine – have no reason to leave you out. Have faith.

Faith is the most prized possession in the three worlds. Faith is the lullaby that helps you to sleep in peace, it is the morning psalm that wakes you up with hope. It is the beautiful poem that makes your heart rhyme. The songs of the birds, the murmuring of a river, fluttering of the leaves – just listen. The stillness of the lake, the blue expanse above you, the tall trees – just see. The sweet smell of the rose, the heady fragrance of jasmine, the mystical sandalwood – just inhale. Be here now. There is hope. There is life.

Finally, look at the vastness of the ocean. It's no more than the size of your hand on the world map. Our giant planet is no more than the size of a tennis ball if our galaxy is a world. Our galaxy is no bigger than a mustard seed in the universe. The whole universe is a tiny dot in infinite creation. Just one tiny dot. Reflect on the immensity of creation.

You are a part of that ordered, impartial and infinite creation. It has nothing against you. Set yourself free to experience how magnificent your existence truly is. That you are breathing means you are wanted, and have a place here. Nature wants you. You are here to be a witness to the wonders and marvels of this world. You are here to be one of the wonders yourself.

Go. Serve and grow. Gratefully.

Notes

1. Pixijane, http://pixijane.deviantart.com/art/Depression-36014878, accessed 1 October 2015. A while ago, someone shared with me an essay on depression. It was an impactful, true, apt and precise account of what it's like to suffer from this disorder. I wrote back, seeking her permission to use it in this book, only to find out that she hadn't actually written it herself. It was an article floating around the Internet, published verbatim on numerous websites and blogs. I contacted many of the writers thereon asking if they were the author of this article. None turned out to be the actual author – they had simply pasted it on their blogs without crediting the original writer. What's worse, two of them actually gave me the permission to use it with one of them claiming to be the original author. Continuing my search, however, I eventually ended up at deviant Art, a website, where this extract was published for the first time (at least according to the date on the website.) It was apparently written by Pixijane (pen-name). I shared it here because I haven't read a better description of depression.

2. Surinder Deol, *The Treasure: A Modern Rendition of Ghalib's Lyrical Love Poetry, A Home Without Doors and Walls*, Partridge Publishing, 2014.

3. Sixteenth-century Spanish saint.
4. I wasn't a monk back then and therefore wasn't called Swami, but since I don't use my old name any more, I've used 'Swami' here.
5. Seventeenth-century English poet.
6. Sixth-century BC Chinese philosopher.
7. Coleman Barks and Michael Green, *The Illuminated Rumi*, Broadway Books, New York, 1997.
8. Allan V. Horwitz and Jerome C. Wakefield, *The Loss of Sadness: How Psychiatry Transformed Normal Sorrow Into Depressive Disorder*, Oxford University Press, New York, 2007.
9. Twentieth-century theoretical physicist.
10. Allan V. Horwitz and Jerome C. Wakefield, *The Loss of Sadness: How Psychiatry Transformed Normal Sorrow Into Depressive Disorder*, Oxford University Press, New York, 2007.
11. https://www.scripps.edu/newsandviews/e_20030929/parsons.html (accessed 1 October 2015).
12. Ancient Chinese philosopher.
13. Fifteenth-century Indian poet.
14. You can read an abridged version of the complete story about how the sage got his vision back in Devi Bhagavatam. A modern literary rendering has been done by Ramesh Menon and published by Rupa Publications. Ramesh Menon, *Devi: The Devi Bhagavatam Retold*, Rupa Publications, New Delhi, 2010.
15. Twentieth-century Welsh poet and writer.
16. On my website, there is a food chart of acidic and alkaline foods, http://omswami.com/wp-content/uploads/2016/01/acid-alkaline-chart.pdf.
17. *Yoga Sutras* of Patanjali, 2. 33–34. *The Threads of Union*, translated by Bon Giovanni.
18. http://www.mkgandhi.org/gquots1.htm (accessed 27 October 2015).
19. https://www.wfp.org/hunger/stats (accessed 27 October 2015).
20. A key scripture to various schools of Hinduism.

21. You can visit my blog (omswami.com) and read up on meditation and various energies.

22. Marianne Williamson, *A Return to Love: Reflections on the Principles of 'A Course in Miracles'*, HarperOne, New York, 1992.

23. Founder of Sikhism and the first Sikh guru.

24. Philippe Verduyn and Saskia Lavrijsen, 'Which emotions last longest and why: The role of event importance and rumination', Springer Science + Business Media, New York, 2014, https:// ppw.kuleuven.be/okp/_pdf/Verduyn2015WELLA.pdf (accessed 1 October 2015).

25. Wikipedia. http://en.wikipedia.org/wiki/Psychomotor_ agitation (accessed 1 October 2015).

26. Warren W. Tyron, *Activity Measurement in Psychology and Medicine*, Springer Publishing, New York, 1991.

27. Based on the *Diagnostic and Statistical Manual of Mental Disorders*, 5th ed. (DSM-V), American Psychiatric Association (APA), Arlington, pp. 160–61.

28. Ibid.

29. Ibid.

30. Eric Maisel, *Rethinking Depression: How to Shed Mental Health Labels and Create Personal Meaning*, New World Library, Novato, California, 2012.

31. Twentieth-century Indian poet.

32. Gerald G. May, *The Dark Night of the Soul*, HarperCollins, New York, 2004.

Made in the USA
San Bernardino, CA
07 January 2018